HOLT SCIENCE & TECHNOLOGY

Earth Science

STUDY GUIDE

HOLT, RINEHART AND WINSTON

A Harcourt Classroom Education Company

Austin • New York • Orlando • Atlanta • San Francisco • Boston • Dallas • Toronto • London

M000250923

To the Student

Are you looking for a way to keep all of your vocabulary terms straight? Do you need practice for an upcoming test? If so, then this booklet is for you. The *Study Guide* is a tool that allows you to confirm what you know and identify topics of difficulty, so that you can succeed in your study of Earth science. These worksheets are reproductions of the Chapter Highlights and Chapter Review sections that follow each chapter in the textbook, with one difference—the *Study Guide* worksheets provide plenty of space for you to record your answers and write down your thoughts and ideas.

■ VOCABULARY & NOTES WORKSHEETS

Vocabulary & Notes Worksheets serve as an important tool to help you organize what you have learned from the chapter. You can use these worksheets
- as a reading guide, to help you identify and study the main concepts of each chapter before or after you read each section;
- as a place to record and review the definitions of important vocabulary terms from each chapter;
- as a reference, to help you study for exams and determine which topics you have learned well and which topics you may need to study further.

■ CHAPTER REVIEW WORKSHEETS

Chapter Review Worksheets give you a chance to practice using what you have a learned from the chapter. You can use these worksheets
- as a learning tool, to work interactively with the textbook by answering the questions that relate to the chapter as you read the text;
- as a review, to test your understanding of the chapter's main concepts and terminology;
- as a practice test, to prepare you for taking the Chapter Test.

Art and Photo Credits
All work, unless otherwise noted, contributed by Holt, Rinehart and Winston.
Abbreviated as follows: (t) top; (b) bottom; (l) left; (r) right; (c) center; (bkgd) background.
Front cover (owl), Kim Taylor/Bruce Coleman, Inc.; (fossil), Barry Rosenthal/FPG International; (fault), David Parker/Science Photo Library/Photo Researchers, Inc.; Page 9 (tc), Sidney Jablonski; 37 (bc), Sidney Jablonski; 58 (tc), David Chapman; 76 (tc), Sidney Jablonski; 85 (t), Ross, Culbert & Lavery; 94 (tc), Sidney Jablonski; 104 (tc), Sidney Jablonski; 114 (tc), Sidney Jablonski; 123 (t), Ross, Culbert & Lavery; 153 (t), George Barile; 169 (bc), Sidney Jablonski; 200 (tc), Sidney Jablonski

Printed in the United States of America

ISBN 0-03-054389-4   4 5 6 7 862 04 03 02

▪ CONTENTS ▪

Chapter 1: **The World of Earth Science**
Vocabulary & Notes Worksheet 1
Chapter Review Worksheet 4

Chapter 2: **Maps as Models of the Earth**
Vocabulary & Notes Worksheet 10
Chapter Review Worksheet 14

Chapter 3: **Minerals of the Earth's Crust**
Vocabulary & Notes Worksheet 20
Chapter Review Worksheet 23

Chapter 4: **Rocks: Mineral Mixtures**
Vocabulary & Notes Worksheet 29
Chapter Review Worksheet 33

Chapter 5: **Energy Resources**
Vocabulary & Notes Worksheet 39
Chapter Review Worksheet 43

Chapter 6: **The Rock and Fossil Record**
Vocabulary & Notes Worksheet 49
Chapter Review Worksheet 53

Chapter 7: **Plate Tectonics**
Vocabulary & Notes Worksheet 59
Chapter Review Worksheet 63

Chapter 8: **Earthquakes**
Vocabulary & Notes Worksheet 69
Chapter Review Worksheet 72

Chapter 9: **Volcanoes**
Vocabulary & Notes Worksheet 77
Chapter Review Worksheet 80

Chapter 10: **Weathering and Soil Formation**
Vocabulary & Notes Worksheet 86
Chapter Review Worksheet 89

Chapter 11: **The Flow of Fresh Water**
Vocabulary & Notes Worksheet 95
Chapter Review Worksheet 99

Chapter 12: **Agents of Erosion and Deposition**
Vocabulary & Notes Worksheet 105
Chapter Review Worksheet 109

Chapter 13: **Exploring the Oceans**
Vocabulary & Notes Worksheet 115
Chapter Review Worksheet 119

CONTENTS, CONTINUED

Chapter 14: The Movement of Ocean Water
Vocabulary & Notes Worksheet 124
Chapter Review Worksheet 128

Chapter 15: The Atmosphere
Vocabulary & Notes Worksheet 134
Chapter Review Worksheet 138

Chapter 16: Understanding Weather
Vocabulary & Notes Worksheet 144
Chapter Review Worksheet 148

Chapter 17: Climate
Vocabulary & Notes Worksheet 154
Chapter Review Worksheet 157

Chapter 18: Observing the Sky
Vocabulary & Notes Worksheet 162
Chapter Review Worksheet 165

Chapter 19: Formation of the Solar System
Vocabulary & Notes Worksheet 171
Chapter Review Worksheet 175

Chapter 20: A Family of Planets
Vocabulary & Notes Worksheet 181
Chapter Review Worksheet 185

Chapter 21: The Universe Beyond
Vocabulary & Notes Worksheet 191
Chapter Review Worksheet 195

Chapter 22: Exploring Space
Vocabulary & Notes Worksheet 201
Chapter Review Worksheet 204

Name _____ Date _____ Class_____

CHAPTER

1 **VOCABULARY & NOTES WORKSHEET**

The World of Earth Science

By studying the Vocabulary and Notes listed for each section below, you can gain a better understanding of this chapter.

SECTION 1

Vocabulary

In your own words, write a definition of each of the following terms in the space provided.

1. geology _____

_____

2. oceanography _____

_____

3. meteorology _____

_____

4. astronomy _____

_____

5. ecosystem _____

_____

Notes

Read the following section highlights. Then, in your own words, write the highlights in your ScienceLog.

- Earth science can be divided into three general categories: geology, oceanography, and meteorology.
- Astronomy is the study of physical things beyond planet Earth.
- Careers in Earth science often require knowledge of more than one science.

SECTION 2

Vocabulary

In your own words, write a definition of each of the following terms in the space provided.

1. scientific method _____

_____

_____

2. observation _____

_____

3. hypothesis _____

_____

Notes

Read the following section highlights. Then, in your own words, write the highlights in your ScienceLog.

• The scientific method is essential for proper scientific investigation.
• Scientists may use the scientific method differently.
• The discovery of *Seismosaurus hallorum* as a new kind of dinosaur was made using the scientific method.
• When scientists finish investigations, it is important that they communicate the results to other scientists.

SECTION 3

Vocabulary

In your own words, write a definition of each of the following terms in the space provided.

1. global warming _____

_____

2. model _____

_____

_____

3. theory _____

_____

_____

Notes

Read the following section highlights. Then, in your own words, write the highlights in your ScienceLog.

• Models are used in science to represent physical things and systems.
• Typically, physical models represent objects, and mathematical models represent systems.
• The global-warming model is a mathematical climate model.
• The greenhouse effect is an important part of the global-warming model.

- Scientists use models to explain the past and present as well as to predict the future.
- The only way to measure the accuracy of a model is to compare predictions based on the model with what actually occurs.

SECTION 4

Vocabulary

In your own words, write a definition of each of the following terms in the space provided.

1. meter _____

_____

_____

_____

2. volume _____

_____

_____

_____

3. mass _____

_____

_____

_____

4. temperature _____

_____

_____

_____

Notes

Read the following section highlights. Then, in your own words, write the highlights in your ScienceLog.

- The International System of Units (SI) helps all scientists share and compare their work.
- The basic SI units of measurement for length, volume, and mass are the meter, cubic meter, and kilogram, respectively.
- To describe temperature, scientists use degrees Celsius (°C) and kelvins (K), which is the SI unit for temperature.

Name _____ Date _____ Class _____

The World of Earth Science

USING VOCABULARY

Use the following terms in a sentence to show that you know what they mean:

1. hypothesis, scientific method _____

_____

_____

_____

2. meteorology, model _____

_____

_____

_____

3. geology, ecosystem _____

_____

_____

_____

4. global warming, oceanography _____

_____

_____

_____

UNDERSTANDING CONCEPTS

Multiple Choice

5. Earth science can be divided into three general categories: meteorology, oceanography, and
- **a.** geography.
- **b.** geology.
- **c.** geochemistry.
- **d.** ecology.

6. The science that deals with fossils is

   a. paleontology.

   b. ecology.

   c. seismology.

   d. volcanology.

7. Meteorology is the study of

   a. meteors.

   b. meteorites.

   c. the atmosphere.

   d. maps.

8. Gillette's hypothesis was

   a. supported by his results.

   b. not supported by his results.

   c. based only on observations.

   d. based only on what he already knew.

9. Two of the most common greenhouse gases are water vapor (H_2O) and

   a. carbon dioxide (CO_2).

   b. krypton (Kr).

   c. radon (Rn).

   d. neon (Ne).

10. Over the past 100 years, the average temperature of Earth's atmosphere has risen about

   a. 10°C.

   b. 5°C.

   c. 1°C.

   d. 0.5°C.

11. The greenhouse effect is used to explain

   a. volcanoes.

   b. earthquakes.

   c. fossilization.

   d. global warming.

12. Global warming would cause

   a. some polar ice to melt.

   b. more rain.

   c. overall rise in sea level.

   d. All of the above

13. An ecosystem can include

   a. plants and animals.

   b. weather and climate.

   c. humans.

   d. All of the above

Short Answer

14. How did Gillette determine that the dinosaur he found was new to science?

_____

_____

_____

_____

_____

15. How and why do scientists use models?

_____

_____

_____

_____

_____

_____

16. Why is the temperature inside a greenhouse usually warmer than the temperature outside?

_____

_____

_____

_____

_____

CONCEPT MAPPING

17. Use the following terms to create a concept map: *Earth science, model, the scientific method, geology, hypothesis, meteorology, oceanography, observation, International System of Units.*

CRITICAL THINKING AND PROBLEM SOLVING

Write one or two sentences to answer the following questions:

18. A rock that contains fossil seashells might be studied by scientists in at least two branches of Earth science. Name those branches. Why did you choose those two?

_____

_____

_____

_____

19. Why might two scientists working on the same problem draw different conclusions?

_____

_____

_____

_____

_____

20. The scientific method often begins with observation. How does observation limit what scientists can study?

_____

_____

_____

_____

_____

21. Why are scientists so careful about making predictions from certain models, such as a global-warming model?

_____

_____

_____

_____

_____

MATH IN SCIENCE

22. Scientists often use scientific laws when constructing models. According to Boyle's law, for example, if you increase the pressure outside a balloon, the balloon will get smaller. This law is expressed as the following formula: $P_1 \times V_1 = P_2 \times V_2$ If the pressure on a balloon (P_1) is one atmosphere (1 atm) and the volume of air in the balloon (V_1) is one liter (1 L), what will the volume be (in liters) if the pressure is increased to 3 atm?

_____

_____

Examine the graph below, and answer the questions that follow.

Atmospheric CO$_2$ (1860–1980)

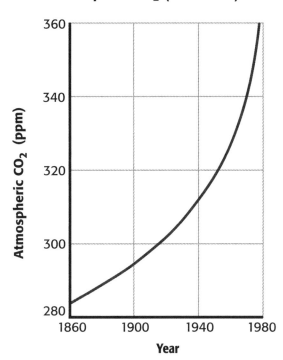

23. Has the amount of CO$_2$ in the atmosphere increased or decreased since 1860?

_____

_____

24. The line on the graph is curved. What does this mean?

_____

_____

25. Was the rate of change in the level of CO$_2$ between 1940 and 1960 higher or lower than it was between 1880 and 1900? How can you tell?

_____

_____

NOW WHAT DO YOU THINK?

Take a minute to review your answers to the ScienceLog questions at the beginning of this chapter. Have your answers changed? If necessary, revise your answers based on what you have learned since you began this chapter.

Name _____ Date _____ Class_____

Maps as Models of the Earth

By studying the Vocabulary and Notes listed for each section below, you can gain a better understanding of this chapter.

SECTION 1

Vocabulary

In your own words, write a definition of each of the following terms in the space provided.

1. map _____

_____

2. true north _____

_____

3. magnetic declination _____

_____

_____

4. equator _____

_____

_____

5. latitude _____

_____

6. longitude _____

_____

7. prime meridian _____

_____

_____

Notes

Read the following section highlights. Then, in your own words, write the highlights in your ScienceLog.

- The North and South Poles are used as reference points for describing direction and location on the Earth.
- The cardinal directions—north, south, east, and west—are used for describing direction.
- Magnetic compasses are used to determine direction on the Earth's surface. The north needle on the compass points to the magnetic north pole.
- Because the geographic North Pole never changes location, it is called true north. The magnetic poles are different from the Earth's geographic poles and have changed location throughout the Earth's history.
- The magnetic declination is the adjustment or difference between magnetic north and geographic north.
- Latitude and longitude are intersecting lines that help you find locations on a map or a globe. Lines of latitude run east-west. Lines of longitude run north-south through the poles.

SECTION 2

Vocabulary

In your own words, write a definition of each of the following terms in the space provided.

1. Mercator projection _____

_____

_____

_____

_____

2. conic projection _____

_____

_____

_____

3. azimuthal projection _____

_____

_____

_____

_____

CHAPTER 2

4. aerial photograph _____

_____

_____

_____

5. remote sensing _____

_____

_____

_____

Notes

Read the following section highlights. Then, in your own words, write the highlights in your ScienceLog.

- A globe is the most accurate representation of the Earth's surface.
- Maps have built-in distortion because some information is lost when mapmakers transfer images from a curved surface to a flat surface.
- Mapmakers use map projections to transfer images of the Earth's curved surface to a flat surface.
- The most common map projections are based on three geometric shapes—cylinders, cones, and planes.
- Remote sensing has allowed mapmakers to make more accurate maps.
- All maps should have a title, date, scale, legend, and north arrow.

SECTION 3

Vocabulary

In your own words, write a definition of each of the following terms in the space provided.

1. topographic map _____

_____

_____

_____

2. elevation _____

_____

_____

Maps as Models of the Earth, continued

3. contour lines _____

_____

_____

_____

4. contour interval _____

_____

_____

_____

_____

5. relief _____

_____

_____

_____

_____

6. index contour _____

_____

_____

_____

Notes

Read the following section highlights. Then, in your own words, write the highlights in your ScienceLog.

- Topographic maps use contour lines to show a mapped area's elevation and the shape and size of landforms.
- The shape of contour lines reflects the shape of the land.
- The contour interval and the spacing of contour lines indicate the slope of the land.
- Like all maps, topographic maps use a set of symbols to represent features of the Earth's surface.
- Contour lines never cross. Contour lines that cross a valley or stream are V-shaped. Contour lines form closed circles around the tops of hills, mountains, and depressions.

CHAPTER 2

CHAPTER

2 **CHAPTER REVIEW WORKSHEET**

Maps as Models of the Earth

USING VOCABULARY

For each pair of terms, explain the difference in their meanings.

1. true north/magnetic north _____

_____

_____

_____

_____

2. latitude/longitude _____

_____

_____

_____

_____

_____

3. equator/prime meridian _____

_____

_____

_____

_____

_____

4. Mercator projection/azimuthal projection _____

_____

_____

_____

_____

_____

Maps as Models of the Earth, continued

5. contour interval/index contour _____

_____

_____

_____

_____

6. elevation/relief _____

_____

_____

_____

_____

UNDERSTANDING CONCEPTS

Multiple Choice

7. A point whose latitude is 0° is located on the
  a. North Pole.
  b. equator.
  c. South Pole.
  d. prime meridian.

8. The distance in degrees east or west of the prime meridian is
  a. latitude.
  b. declination.
  c. longitude
  d. projection.

9. The needle of a magnetic compass points toward the
  a. meridians.
  b. parallels.
  c. geographic North Pole.
  d. magnetic north pole.

10. The most common map projections are based on three geometric shapes. Which of the following geometric shapes is not one of them?
  a. cylinder
  b. square
  c. cone
  d. plane

11. A Mercator projection is distorted near the
   a. equator.
   b. poles.
   c. prime meridian.
   d. date line.

12. What kind of scale does not have written units of measure?
   a. representative fraction
   b. verbal
   c. graphic
   d. mathematical

13. What is the relationship between the distance on a map and the actual distance on the Earth called?
   a. legend
   b. elevation
   c. relief
   d. scale

14. The latitude of the North Pole is
   a. 100° north.   **c.** 180° north.
   b. 90° north.   **d.** 90° south.

15. Widely spaced contour lines indicate a
   a. steep slope.   **c.** hill.
   b. gentle slope.   **d.** river.

16. _____ is the height of an object above sea level.
   a. Contour interval
   b. Elevation
   c. Declination
   d. Index contour

Short Answer

17. How can a magnetic compass be used to find direction on the Earth's surface?

_____

_____

_____

_____

18. Why is a map legend important?

_____

_____

Maps as Models of the Earth, continued

19. Why does Greenland appear so large in relation to other landmasses on a map with a Mercator projection?

_____

_____

_____

_____

20. What is the function of contour lines on a topographic map?

_____

_____

_____

CONCEPT MAPPING

21. Use the following terms to create a concept map: *maps, legend, map projection, map parts, scale, cylinder, title, cone, plane, date, north arrow.*

CHAPTER 2

CRITICAL THINKING AND PROBLEM SOLVING

Write one or two sentences to answer the following questions:

22. One of the important parts of a map is its date. Why is this so important?

_____

_____

_____

_____

23. A mapmaker has to draw one map for three different countries that do not share a common unit of measure. What type of scale would this mapmaker use? Why?

_____

_____

_____

_____

_____

24. How would a topographic map of the Rocky Mountains differ from a topographic map of the Great Plains?

_____

_____

_____

_____

_____

MATH IN SCIENCE

25. A map has a verbal scale of 1 cm equals 200 m. If the actual distance between two points is 12,000 m, how far apart will they appear on the map?

_____

_____

_____

Maps as Models of the Earth, *continued*

26. On a topographic map, the contour interval is 50 ft. The bottom of a mountain begins on a contour line marked with a value of 1,050 ft. The top of the mountain is within a contour line that is 12 lines higher than the bottom of the mountain. What is the elevation of the top of the mountain?

_____

_____

_____

INTERPRETING GRAPHICS

Use the topographic map on page 53 of your textbook to answer the questions that follow.

27. What is the elevation change between two adjacent lines on this map?

_____

_____

28. What type of relief does this area have?

_____

_____

29. What surface features are shown on this map?

_____

_____

30. What is the elevation at the top of Ore Hill?

_____

_____

NOW WHAT DO YOU THINK?

Take a minute to review your answers to the ScienceLog questions at the beginning of this chapter. Have your answers changed? If necessary, revise your answers based on what you have learned since you began this chapter.

CHAPTER 2

CHAPTER

3 VOCABULARY & NOTES WORKSHEET

Minerals of the Earth's Crust

October - Opal

By studying the Vocabulary and Notes listed for each section below, you can gain a better understanding of this chapter.

SECTION 1

Rocks are made of minerals, but minerals aren't made of rocks.

Vocabulary

In your own words, write a definition of each of the following terms in the space provided.

1. mineral- *a naturally formed inorganic solid with a crystilline structure*

2. element- *pure substances that can't be broken down into simpler substances by ordinary chemical means*

3. atom - *the smallest part of an element that still has the original properties of the element*

4. compound - *a substance made of two or more elements that have been chemically joined or bonded together*

5. crystal - *solid geometric forms of minerals in a repeating pattern of atoms that is present throughout the mineral*

6. silicate mineral - *minerals that contain a combination of silicon + oxygen*

- Make up more than 90% of the Earth's Crust.

Minerals of the Earth's Crust, continued

7. nonsilicate mineral _dont contain combination of silicon + oxigen._

Notes

Read the following section highlights. Then, in your own words, write the highlights in your ScienceLog.

- A mineral is a naturally formed, inorganic solid with a definite crystalline structure.
- An atom is the smallest unit of an element that retains the properties of the element.
- A compound forms when atoms of two or more elements bond together chemically.
- Every mineral has a unique crystalline structure. The crystal class a mineral belongs to is directly related to the mineral's chemical composition.
- Minerals are classified as either silicates or nonsilicates. Each group includes different types of minerals.

SECTION 2

Vocabulary

In your own words, write a definition of each of the following terms in the space provided.

1. luster _the way a surface reflects light._

2. streak _The color of the mineral in a powder form._

3. cleavage _The tendancy for some minerals to break along flat surfaces._

4. fracture _The tendancy for some minerals to break unevenly along irregular patterns or surfaces._

5. hardness _the minerals resistance to being scratched._

—Mo's Hardness Scale
— Talc, 1; Diamond, 10

CHAPTER 3

6. density — *The measure of how much matter is in a given ammount of space*

Notes

Read the following section highlights. Then, in your own words, write the highlights in your ScienceLog.

- Color is not a reliable indicator for identifying minerals.
- The luster of a mineral can be metallic, submetallic, or nonmetallic.
- A mineral's streak does not necessarily match its surface color.
- The way a mineral breaks can be used to determine its identity. Cleavage and fracture are two ways that minerals break.
- Mohs' hardness scale provides a numerical rating for the hardness of minerals.
- The density of a mineral can be used to identify it.
- Some minerals have special properties that can be used to quickly identify them.

gem- valuable highly priced mineral that is rare or diffucult to obtain

SECTION 3

Vocabulary

In your own words, write a definition of each of the following terms in the space provided.

1. ore — *mineral deposit large enough + pure enough to be mined for a profit.*

2. reclamation — *the process of returning land to its original state*

Notes

Read the following section highlights. Then, in your own words, write the highlights in your ScienceLog.

- Minerals form in both underground environments and surface environments.
- Two main types of mining are surface mining and deep mining.
- Minerals are valuable because metals can be extracted from them and because some of them can be cut to form gems.
- Reclamation is the process of returning mined land to its original state.

Name _____ Date _____ Class_____

CHAPTER

3 **CHAPTER REVIEW WORKSHEET**

Minerals of the Earth's Crust

USING VOCABULARY   How do we define minerals

For each pair of terms, explain the difference in their meanings.

1. fracture/cleavage _____

       1) Occur naturally _____

       2) Are inorganic _____

       3) Have unique chemical compositions.

2. element/compound _____ 4) Have a crystalline structure

_____

_____

_____

3. color/streak _____

_____

_____

_____

4. density/hardness _____

_____

_____

_____

5. silicate mineral/nonsilicate mineral _____

_____

_____

_____

6. mineral/atom _____

_____

_____

_____

CHAPTER 3

UNDERSTANDING CONCEPTS

Multiple Choice

7. On Mohs' hardness scale, which of the following minerals is harder than quartz?

   a. talc
   b. apatite
   c. gypsum
   d. topaz

8. A mineral's streak

   a. is more reliable than color in identifying a mineral.
   b. reveals the mineral's specific gravity.
   c. is the same as a luster test.
   d. reveals the mineral's crystal structure.

9. Which of the following factors is NOT important in the formation of minerals?

   a. heat
   b. volcanic activity
   c. presence of ground water
   d. wind

10. Which of the following terms is NOT used to describe a mineral's luster?

   a. pearly
   b. waxy
   c. dull
   d. hexagonal

11. Which of the following is considered a special property that applies to only a few minerals?

   a. color
   b. luster
   c. streak
   d. magnetism

12. Which of the following physical properties can be expressed in numbers?

   a. luster
   b. hardness
   c. color
   d. reaction to acid

13. Which of the following minerals would scratch fluorite?

   a. talc
   b. quartz
   c. gypsum
   d. calcite

Minerals of the Earth's Crust, continued

Short Answer

14. Using no more than 25 words, define the term _mineral._

_____

_____

15. In one sentence, describe how density is used to identify a mineral.

_____

_____

16. What methods of mineral identification are the most reliable? Explain.

_____

_____

_____

_____

CONCEPT MAPPING

17. Use the following terms to create a concept map: _minerals, oxides, nonsilicates, carbonates, silicates, hematite, calcite, quartz._

▲▲ CHAPTER 3
▲ ▲

CRITICAL THINKING AND PROBLEM SOLVING

Write one or two sentences to answer the following questions:

18. Suppose you have three rings, each with a different gem. One has a diamond, one has an amethyst (purple quartz), and one has a topaz. You mail the rings in a small box to your friend who lives five states away. When the box arrives at its destination, two of the gems are damaged. One gem, however, is damaged much worse than the other. What scientific reason can you give for the difference in damage?

_____

_____

_____

_____

_____

_____

_____

_____

19. While trying to determine the identity of a mineral, you decide to do a streak test. You rub the mineral across the plate, but it does not leave a streak. Does this mean your test failed? Explain your answer.

_____

_____

_____

_____

_____

_____

_____

_____

Minerals of the Earth's Crust, continued

20. Imagine that you work at a jeweler's shop and someone brings in some "gold nuggets" that they want to sell. The person claims that an old prospector found the gold nuggets during the California gold rush. You are not sure if the nuggets are real gold. How would you decide whether to buy the nuggets? Which identification tests would help you decide the nuggets' identity?

_____

_____

_____

_____

_____

_____

_____

21. Suppose that you find a mineral crystal that is as tall as you are. What kinds of environmental factors would cause such a crystal to form?

_____

_____

_____

_____

_____

_____

_____

MATH IN SCIENCE

22. Gold has a specific gravity of 19. Pyrite's specific gravity is 5. How much denser is gold than pyrite?

_____

_____

_____

_____

CHAPTER 3

Minerals of the Earth's Crust, continued

23. In a quartz crystal there is one silicon atom for every two oxygen atoms. That means that the ratio of silicon atoms to oxygen atoms is 1:2. If there were 8 million oxygen atoms in a sample of quartz, how many silicon atoms would there be?

_____

_____

INTERPRETING GRAPHICS

Imagine that you had a sample of feldspar and analyzed it to find out what it is made of. The results of your analysis are shown below.

24. Your sample consists of four elements. What percentage of each one is your sample made of?

_____

_____

_____

_____

25. If your mineral sample has a mass of 10 g, how many grams of oxygen does it contain?

_____

26. Make a circle graph showing how much of each of the four elements the feldspar contains. (You will find help on making circle graphs in the Appendix of your textbook.)

NOW WHAT DO YOU THINK?

Take a minute to review your answers to the ScienceLog questions at the beginning of this chapter. Have your answers changed? If necessary, revise your answers based on what you have learned since you began this chapter.

Rocks: Mineral Mixtures

By studying the Vocabulary and Notes listed for each section below, you can gain a better understanding of this chapter.

SECTION 1

Vocabulary

In your own words, write a definition of each of the following terms in the space provided.

1. rock _— the solid mixture of crystals of one or more minerals._

2. rock cycle _— the process at which one type of rock changes into another_

3. magma _— the hot liquid that forms when rock ~~partially or completed~~ melts._
lava — magma that flows on Earth's surface

4. sedimentary rock _— rocks formed when sediments are packed + cemented together._

5. metamorphic rock _— rock that forms when the texture and composition of a pre-existing rock is changed by heat or pressure underground._

▲ ▲ **CHAPTER 4**

6. igneous rock _the rock that forms from cooling magma._

Comes from latin word for "fire"

7. composition _minerals a rock is made of._

8. texture _determined by the size, shapes, and positions of the grains of which it was made._

Notes

Read the following section highlights. Then, in your own words, write the highlights in your ScienceLog.

- Rocks have been used by humans for thousands of years, and they are just as valuable today.
- Rocks are classified into three main types—igneous, sedimentary, and metamorphic—depending on how they formed.
- The rock cycle describes the process by which a rock can change from one rock type to another.
- Scientists further classify rocks according to two criteria—composition and texture.
- Molten igneous material creates rock formations both below and above ground.

Rocks: Mineral Mixtures, continued

SECTION 2

Vocabulary

In your own words, write a definition of each of the following terms in the space provided.

1. intrusive — *when magma cools beneath the Earth's surface.*

Coarse grained bc its well insulated + cools slowly.

2. extrusive — *rocks that form on the Earth's surface.*

Cools quickly + contains small crystals or none at all.

Notes

Read the following section highlights. Then, in your own words, write the highlights in your ScienceLog.

- The texture of igneous rock is determined by the rate at which it cools. The slower magma cools, the larger the crystals are.
- Felsic igneous rock is light-colored and lightweight, while mafic igneous rock is dark-colored and heavy.
- Igneous material that solidifies at the Earth's surface is called extrusive, while igneous material that solidifies within the crust is called intrusive.

SECTION 3

Vocabulary

In your own words, write a definition of each of the following terms in the space provided.

1. strata *layers of rock (sedimentary)*

2. stratification *layering of rock*

▲ ▲ CHAPTER 4

Notes

Read the following section highlights. Then, in your own words, write the highlights in your ScienceLog.

• Clastic sedimentary rock is made of rock and mineral fragments that are compacted and cemented together. Chemical sedimentary rock forms from minerals that crystallize out of a solution such as sea water. Organic sedimentary rock forms from the remains of organisms.

• Sedimentary rocks record the history of their formation in their features. Some common features are strata, ripple marks, and fossils.

SECTION 4
Vocabulary

metaparphic — meta means change + morpha means shape

In your own words, write a definition of each of the following terms in the space provided.

1. foliated *— metamorphic rock that consists of aligned minerals.*

_____

_____

2. nonfoliated *— m metamorphic rock that dosen't have a regular pattern.*

Notes

Read the following section highlights. Then, in your own words, write the highlights in your ScienceLog.

• One type of metamorphism is the result of magma heating small areas of surrounding rock, changing its texture and composition.

• Most metamorphism is the product of heat and pressure acting on large regions of the Earth's crust.

• The mineral composition of a rock changes when the minerals it is made of recrystallize to form new minerals. These new minerals are more stable under increased temperature and pressure.

• Metamorphic rock that contains aligned mineral grains is called foliated, and metamorphic rock that does not contain aligned mineral grains is called nonfoliated.

Name _____ Date _____ Class _____

Rocks: Mineral Mixtures

USING VOCABULARY

To complete the following sentences, choose the correct term from each pair of terms listed below, and write the term in the space provided.

1. _____ igneous rock is more likely to have coarse-grained texture than _____ igneous rock. (Extrusive/intrusive or Intrusive/extrusive)

2. _____ metamorphic rock texture consists of parallel alignment of mineral grains. (Foliated or Nonfoliated)

3. _____ sedimentary rock forms when grains of sand become cemented together. (Clastic or Chemical)

4. _____ cools quickly on the Earth's surface. (Lava or Magma)

5. Strata are found in _____ rock. (igneous or sedimentary)

UNDERSTANDING CONCEPTS

Multiple Choice

6. A type of rock that forms deep within the Earth when magma solidifies is called
   a. sedimentary.
   b. metamorphic.
   c. organic.
   d. igneous.

7. A type of rock that forms under high temperature and pressure but is not exposed to enough heat to melt the rock is
   a. sedimentary.   c. organic.
   b. metamorphic.   d. igneous.

8. After they are deposited, sediments, such as sand, are turned into sedimentary rock when they are compacted and
   a. cemented.
   b. metamorphosed.
   c. melted.
   d. weathered.

9. An igneous rock with a coarse-grained texture forms when
   a. magma cools very slowly.
   b. magma cools very quickly.
   c. magma cools quickly, then slowly.
   d. magma cools slowly, then quickly.

10. The layering that occurs in sedimentary rock is called
    a. foliation.   c. stratification.
    b. ripple marks.   d. compaction.

▲▲ CHAPTER 4

11. An example of a clastic sedimentary rock is
  a. obsidian.
  b. sandstone.
  c. gneiss.
  d. marble.

12. A common sedimentary rock structure is
  a. a sill.
  b. a pluton.
  c. cross-bedding.
  d. a lava flow.

13. An example of mafic igneous rock is
  a. granite.   **c.** quartzite.
  b. basalt.   **d.** pumice.

14. Chemical sedimentary rock forms when
  a. magma cools and solidifies.
  b. minerals are twisted into a new arrangement.
  c. minerals crystallize from a solution.
  d. sand grains are cemented together.

15. Which of the following is a foliated metamorphic rock?
  a. sandstone   **c.** shale
  b. gneiss   **d.** basalt

Short Answer

16. In no more than three sentences, explain the rock cycle.

_____

_____

_____

_____

_____

_____

17. How are sandstone and siltstone different from one another? How are they the same?

_____

_____

_____

_____

18. In one or two sentences, explain how the cooling rate of magma affects the texture of the igneous rock that is formed.

_____

_____

_____

_____

_____

_____

CONCEPT MAPPING

19. Use the following terms to create a concept map: *rocks, clastic, metamorphic, nonfoliated, igneous, intrusive, chemical, foliated, extrusive, organic, sedimentary.*

Rocks: Mineral Mixtures, continued

CRITICAL THINKING AND PROBLEM SOLVING

Write one or two sentences to answer the following questions:

20. The sedimentary rock coquina is made up of pieces of seashells. Which of the three kinds of sedimentary rock could it be? Explain.

_____

_____

_____

_____

_____

_____

_____

21. If you were looking for fossils in the rocks around your home and the rock type that was closest to your home was metamorphic, would you find many fossils? Why or why not?

_____

_____

_____

_____

_____

_____

22. Suppose you are writing a book about another planet. In your book, you mention that the planet has no atmosphere or weather. Which type of rock will you not find on the planet? Explain.

_____

_____

_____

_____

_____

_____

Rocks: Mineral Mixtures, continued

23. Imagine that you want to quarry or mine granite. You have all of the equipment, but you need a place to quarry. You have two pieces of land to choose from. One piece is described as having a granite batholith under it, and the other has a granite sill. If both plutonic bodies were at the same depth, which one would be a better buy for you? Explain your answer.

_____

_____

_____

_____

_____

MATH IN SCIENCE

24. If a 60 kg granite boulder were broken down into sand grains and if quartz made up 35 percent of the boulder's mass, how many kilograms of the resulting sand would be quartz grains?

_____

_____

_____

INTERPRETING GRAPHICS

The curve on the graph below shows how the melting point of a particular rock changes with increasing temperature and pressure. Use the graph to answer the questions that follow.

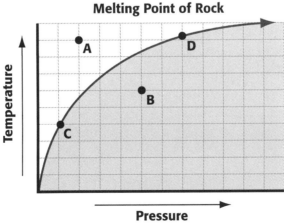

► ► CHAPTER 4
▲ ▲

25. What type of material, liquid or solid, would you find at point A? Why?

_____

_____

_____

26. What would you find at point B?

_____

_____

27. Points C and D represent different temperature and pressure conditions for a single, solid rock. Why does this rock have a higher melting temperature at point D than it does at point C?

_____

_____

_____

_____

NOW WHAT DO YOU THINK?

Take a minute to review your answers to the ScienceLog questions at the beginning of this chapter. Have your answers changed? If necessary, revise the answers based on what you have learned since you began this chapter.

CHAPTER

5 VOCABULARY & NOTES WORKSHEET

Energy Resources

By studying the Vocabulary and Notes listed for each section below, you can gain a better understanding of this chapter.

SECTION 1
Vocabulary
In your own words, write a definition of each of the following terms in the space provided.

1. natural resource _____

_____

_____

_____

2. renewable resource _____

_____

_____

_____

3. nonrenewable resource _____

_____

_____

_____

4. recycling _____

_____

_____

Notes
Read the following section highlights. Then, in your own words, write the highlights in your ScienceLog.
- Natural resources include everything that is not made by humans and that can be used by organisms.
- Renewable resources, like trees and water, can be replaced in a relatively short period of time.
- Nonrenewable resources cannot be replaced, or they take a very long time to replace.
- Recycling reduces the amount of natural resources that must be obtained from the Earth.

SECTION 2

Vocabulary

In your own words, write a definition of each of the following terms in the space provided.

1. energy resource _____

_____

_____

_____

2. fossil fuel _____

_____

_____

_____

3. petroleum _____

_____

_____

_____

4. natural gas _____

_____

_____

_____

5. coal _____

_____

_____

_____

6. strip mining _____

_____

_____

_____

_____

Energy Resources, continued

_____

7. acid precipitation _____

_____

_____

8. smog _____

_____

_____

Notes

Read the following section highlights. Then, in your own words, write the highlights in your ScienceLog.

• Fossil fuels, including petroleum, natural gas, and coal, form from the buried remains of once-living organisms.

• Petroleum and natural gas form mainly from the remains of microscopic sea life.

• Coal forms from decayed swamp plants and varies in quality based on its percentage of carbon.

• Petroleum and natural gas are obtained through drilling, while coal is obtained through mining.

• Obtaining and using fossil fuels can cause many environmental problems, including acid precipitation, water pollution, smog, and the release of excess carbon dioxide.

SECTION 3

Vocabulary

In your own words, write a definition of each of the following terms in the space provided.

1. nuclear energy _____

_____

_____

_____

2. solar energy _____

_____

_____

3. wind energy _____

_____

_____

4. hydroelectric energy _____

_____

_____

_____

5. biomass _____

_____

_____

6. gasohol _____

_____

_____

7. geothermal energy _____

_____

_____

Notes

Read the following section highlights. Then, in your own words, write the highlights in your ScienceLog.

- Nuclear energy is most often produced by fission.
- Radioactive wastes and the threat of overheating in nuclear power plants are among the major problems associated with using nuclear energy.
- Solar energy can be converted to electricity by using solar cells.
- Solar energy can be used for direct heating by using solar collectors.
- Solar energy can be converted to electricity on both small and large scales.
- Although harnessing wind energy is practical only in certain areas, the process produces no air pollutants, and land on wind farms can be used for more than one purpose.
- Hydroelectric energy is inexpensive, renewable, and produces little pollution. However, hydroelectric dams can damage wildlife habitats, create erosion problems, and decrease water quality.
- Plant material and animal dung that contains plant material can be burned to release energy.
- Some plant material can be converted to alcohol. This alcohol can be mixed with gasoline to make a fuel mixture called gasohol.
- Geothermal energy can be harnessed from hot, liquid water and steam that escape through natural vents or through wells drilled into the Earth's crust. This energy can be used for direct heating or can be converted to electricity.

5 CHAPTER REVIEW WORKSHEET

Energy Resources

USING VOCABULARY

For each pair of terms, explain the difference in their meanings.

1. natural resource/energy resource _____

_____

_____

_____

_____

2. acid precipitation/smog _____

_____

_____

_____

_____

3. biomass/gasohol _____

_____

_____

_____

_____

_____

4. hydroelectric energy/geothermal energy _____

_____

_____

_____

_____

UNDERSTANDING CONCEPTS

Multiple Choice

5. Of the following, the one that is a renewable resource is

    a. coal.

    b. trees.

    c. oil.

    d. natural gas.

6. All of the following are separated from petroleum except

    a. jet fuel.

    b. lignite.

    c. kerosene.

    d. fuel oil.

7. Which of the following is a component of natural gas?

    a. gasohol

    b. methane

    c. kerosene

    d. gasoline

8. Peat, lignite, and anthracite are all stages in the formation of

    a. petroleum.

    b. natural gas.

    c. coal.

    d. gasohol.

9. Which of the following factors contribute to smog problems?

    a. high numbers of automobiles

    b. lots of sunlight

    c. mountains surrounding urban areas

    d. All of the above

10. Which of the following resources produces the least pollution?

    a. solar energy

    b. natural gas

    c. nuclear energy

    d. petroleum

11. Nuclear power plants use a process called _____ to produce energy.

    a. fission

    b. fusion

    c. fractionation

    d. None of the above

12. A solar-powered calculator uses

    a. solar collectors.

    b. solar panels.

    c. solar mirrors.

    d. solar cells.

13. Which of the following is a problem with using wind energy?

    a. air pollution

    b. amount of land required for wind turbines

    c. limited locations for wind farms

    d. None of the above

14. Dung is a type of

    a. geothermal energy.

    b. gasohol.

    c. biomass.

    d. None of the above

Energy Resources, continued

Short Answer

15. Because renewable resources can be replaced, why do we need to conserve them?

_____

_____

16. How does acid precipitation form?

_____

_____

_____

17. If sunlight is free, why is electricity from solar cells expensive?

_____

_____

CONCEPT MAPPING

18. Use the following terms to create a concept map: *fossil fuels, wind energy, energy resources, biomass, renewable resources, solar energy, nonrenewable resources, natural gas, gasohol, coal, oil.*

CRITICAL THINKING AND PROBLEM SOLVING

Write one or two sentences to answer the following questions:

19. How would your life be different if all fossil fuels suddenly disappeared?

_____

_____

_____

_____

20. Are fossil fuels really nonrenewable? Explain.

_____

_____

_____

_____

_____

21. What solutions are there for the problems associated with nuclear waste?

_____

_____

_____

_____

22. How could the problems associated with the dams in Washington and local fish populations be solved?

_____

_____

_____

_____

_____

23. What limits might there be on the productivity of a geothermal power plant?

_____

_____

_____

_____

_____

_____

MATH IN SCIENCE

24. Imagine that you are designing a solar car. If you mount solar cells on the underside of the car as well as on the top in direct sunlight, and it takes five times as many cells underneath to generate the same amount of electricity generated by the cells on top, what percentage of the sunlight is reflected back off the pavement?

_____

_____

_____

INTERPRETING GRAPHICS

The chart below shows how various energy resources meet the world's energy needs. Use the chart to answer the questions that follow.

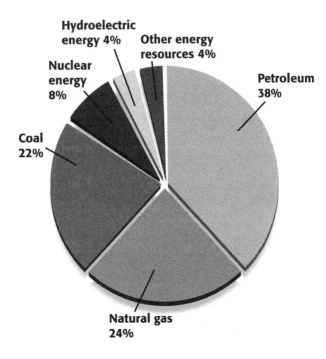

25. What percentage of the world's total energy needs is met by coal?

_____

_____

by natural gas?

_____

_____

by hydroelectric energy?

_____

_____

26. What percentage of the world's total energy needs is met by fossil fuels?

_____

_____

27. How much more of the world's total energy needs is met by petroleum than by natural gas?

_____

_____

NOW WHAT DO YOU THINK?

Take a minute to review your answers to the ScienceLog questions at the beginning of this chapter. Have your answers changed? If necessary, revise your answers based on what you have learned since you began this chapter.

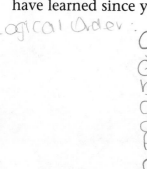

CHAPTER

6 **VOCABULARY & NOTES WORKSHEET**

The Rock and Fossil Record

By studying the Vocabulary and Notes listed for each section below, you can gain a better understanding of this chapter.

SECTION 1

Vocabulary

In your own words, write a definition for the following terms in the space provided.

1. uniformitarianism —a principle that states that the same geological process shaping the Earth today have been at work through out Earth's history.

2. catastrophism —a principle that states that all geographic change occurs suddenly.

Notes

Read the following section highlights. Then, in your own words, write the highlights in your ScienceLog.

• Scientists use the principle of uniformitarianism to interpret the past and make predictions.

• According to uniformitarianism, geologic change is gradual. According to catastrophism, geologic change is sudden.

• Before Hutton and Lyell, most scientists believed all geologic change was catastrophic. After Hutton and Lyell, most scientists rejected catastrophism. Today most scientists favor uniformitarianism, but they recognize some geologic change as catastrophic.

SECTION 2

Vocabulary

In your own words, write a definition for the following terms in the space provided.

1. relative dating —determining wether an object or event is older or younger than other objects or events.

2. superposition —principle that states that younger rocks lie above older rocks.

Name _____ Date _____ Class _____

The Rock and Fossil Record, continued

3. geologic column —an ideal sequence of rock layers that contain all the known fossil + rock formations on Earth from oldest to youngest

4. unconformity —a surface that represents a missing part of the geologic column.

Notes

Read the following section highlights. Then, in your own words, write the highlights in your ScienceLog.

- Geologists use relative dating to determine the relative age of objects.
- Geologists assume that younger layers lie above older layers in undisturbed rock-layer sequences. This is called superposition.
- The entire rock and fossil record is represented by the geologic column.
- Geologists examine the relationships between rock layers and the structures that cut across them in order to determine relative ages.
- Geologists also determine relative ages by assuming that all rock layers were originally horizontal.
- Unconformities form where rock layers are missing, and they represent time that is not recorded in the rock record.

SECTION 3

Vocabulary

In your own words, write a definition for the following terms in the space provided.

1. absolute dating —a process of establishing the age of an object, such as a fossil or rock layer, by determining the # of years it had existed

2. isotopes —atoms of the same element that have the same # of protons but diff. # of neutrons

3. radioactive decay —radioactive isotopes tend to break down into stable isotopes of other elements in a process called decay.

4. radiometric dating _determining the absolute age of a sample based on the ratio of parent material to daughter material._

5. half-life _the time it takes for one half of a radioactive sample to decay._

Notes

Read the following section highlights. Then, in your own words, write the highlights in your ScienceLog.

- During radioactive decay, an unstable parent isotope of one element decays at a constant rate into a stable daughter isotope of a different element.
- The absolute age of samples of some rocks and fossils can be determined by the ratio of unstable isotopes to stable isotopes in the samples. This is called radiometric dating.
- The radiometric-dating method scientists use depends on the estimated age of the object they are dating.

SECTION 4

Vocabulary

In your own words, write a definition for the following terms in the space provided.

1. fossil _any naturally preserved evidence of life_

2. permineralization _process in which minerals fill in pore spaces of an organism._

3. petrification _occurs when the organism's tissues are completely replaced by minerals._

4. trace fossil _any naturally preserved evidence of an animal's activity._

5. coprolites _preserved feces or dung of an animal_

6. mold _cavity in the ground or rock where a plant or animal was buried._

7. cast _an object created when sediment fills a mold + becomes a rock_

amber- hardened tree sap.

The Rock and Fossil Record, continued

8. index fossil *- are fossils of organisms that lived during a realitavely short, well-defined timespan.*

Notes

Read the following section highlights. Then, in your own words, write the highlights in your ScienceLog.

- Any naturally preserved evidence of life is considered a fossil.
- There are many ways fossils can form, such as mineral replacement, mummification, and freezing.
- Fossils can be used to show how environments and organisms have changed over time.
- Fossils, especially index fossils, can be used to date rocks.

SECTION 5

Vocabulary

In your own words, write a definition for the following terms in the space provided.

1. geologic time scale *- scale that divides Earth's 4.6 billion year history into distinct intervals of time.*

2. eon *- the largest division of geologic time.; 4 eons are divided into eras.*

3. era *- 2nd largest division of geologic time.*

4. period *- Eras are divided into periods, which are the 3rd largest division of geologic time.*

5. epoch *- some periods are divided into epochs, which is the 4th division of geologic time.*

Notes

- The history of the Earth is recorded in rock layers.
- The 4.6 billion years of Earth's history is represented on the geologic time scale, including the intervals not represented in the rock and fossil record.
- There are several different time intervals on the geologic time scale.
- Scientists know very little about the Earth's history. This is because the rock and fossil record primarily represents the last eon of Earth's history.

Name _____ Date _____ Class_____

CHAPTER

6 CHAPTER REVIEW WORKSHEET

The Rock and Fossil Record

USING VOCABULARY

For each pair of terms, explain the difference in their meaning.

1. uniformitarianism/catastrophism _Fault- break in Earth's crust in which blocks of crust slide realitive to one another_

intrusion- when molten rock from the earth's interior squeezes into existing rock + cools

2. relative dating/absolute dating _folding- occurs when rocks bend + buckle_

tilting- occurs when internal forces in the Earth slant rock layers without folding them.

paleozoic- "old life" lasted from 540-248 million years ago.

3. mold/cast

mesozoic - "middle life" lasted until about 65 million years ago

4. eon/era _mesozoic era was the "age of the reptiles"_

cenozoic- "recent life" started 65 million years ago until now. "Age of the Mamals"

CHAPTER 6

Copyright © by Holt, Rinehart and Winston. All rights reserved.

STUDY GUIDE **53**

5. geologic time scale/geologic column _____

_____

_____

_____

_____

_____

UNDERSTANDING CONCEPTS

Multiple Choice

6. Which of the following words does not describe catastrophic geologic change?

    a. sudden   **c.** gradual

    b. widespread   **d.** time

7. Scientists assign relative ages by using

    a. potassium-argon dating.

    b. the principle of superposition.

    c. radioactive half-lives.

    d. the ratios of isotopes.

8. Rock layers cut by a fault formed

    a. after the fault.

    b. before the fault.

    c. at the same time as the fault.

    d. Cannot be determined

9. If the half-life of an unstable element is 5,000 years, what percentage of the parent material will be left after 10,000 years?

    a. 100   **c.** 50

    b. 75   **d.** 25

10. Of the following unstable isotopes, which has the longest half-life?

    a. uranium-238

    b. potassium-40

    c. carbon-14

11. Fossils can be

    a. petrified.

    b. dried out.

    c. frozen.

    d. All of the above

12. Of the following geologic time intervals, which is the shortest?

    a. an eon

    b. a period

    c. an era

    d. an epoch

13. If Earth's history is put on a scale of 12 hours, human civilizations would have been around for

    a. hours.

    b. minutes.

    c. less than 1 second.

Short Answer

14. What is the principle of superposition? How is it used by geologists?

_____

_____

_____

_____

_____

15. Describe how plant and animal remains become petrified.

_____

_____

_____

16. Explain how a fossil cast forms.

_____

_____

_____

CONCEPT MAPPING

17. Use the following terms to create a concept map: *age, absolute dating, half-life, radioactive decay, radiometric dating, relative dating, superposition, geologic column, isotopes.*

CRITICAL THINKING AND PROBLEM SOLVING

Write one or two sentences to answer the following questions:

18. You may have heard the term *petrified wood*. Why doesn't a "petrified" tree contain any wood?

_____

_____

_____

19. How do tracks and burrows end up in the rock and fossil record?

_____

_____

_____

20. How do you know that an intrusion is younger than its surrounding rock layers?

_____

_____

_____

MATH IN SCIENCE

21. On the graph below place a dot on the *y*-axis at 100 percent. Then place a dot on the graph at each half-life to show how much of the parent material is left. Connect the points with a curved line.

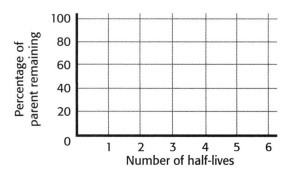

Will the percentage of parent material ever reach zero? Explain.

_____

_____

_____

The Rock and Fossil Record, continued

INTERPRETING GRAPHICS

Examine the drawing below, and answer the following questions.

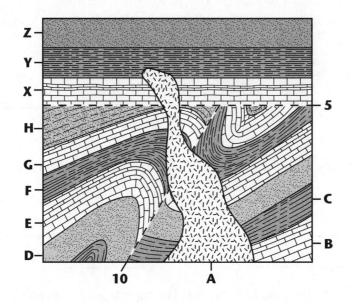

22. Is intrusion A younger or older than layer X?

_____

23. What kind of unconformity is marked by 5?

_____

24. Is intrusion A younger or older than fault 10? Why?

_____

_____

25. Other than the intrusion and faulting, what event occurred in layers B, C, D, E, F, G, and H? Number this event, the intrusion, and the faulting in the order they occurred.

_____

_____

NOW WHAT DO YOU THINK?

Take a minute to review your answers to the ScienceLog questions at the beginning of the chapter. Have your answers changed? If necessary, revise your answers based on what you have learned since you began this chapter. Record your revisions in your ScienceLog.

CHAPTER

7 **VOCABULARY & NOTES WORKSHEET**

Plate Tectonics

By studying the Vocabulary and Notes listed for each section below, you can gain a better understanding of this chapter.

SECTION 1

Vocabulary

In your own words, write a definition of each of the following terms in the space provided.

1. crust — Outermost + thinnest layer. 5-100km thick. We live here

2. mantle — its in the middle of the Earth, and contains most of the earths mass. It is 2900 km thick.

3. core — extends from bottom of mantle to the center of the Earth

4. lithosphere — "rockSphere" Contains crust and rigid part of the mantle It's divided into tectonic plates + is the thinnest layer

5. asthenosphere — "weak sphere" Soft layer of the mantle that flows the same rate your fingernails grow

6. mesosphere — "middle sphere" The strong lower part of the mantle + the thickest layer.

7. outer core — liquid layer below the mantle

8. inner core — Solid dense center of the earth.

9. tectonic plates — pieces of the lithosphere that move around on top of the asthenosphere

• Seismic waves are vibrations that travel through the earth

_____

Plate Tectonics, continued

_____

Notes

Read the following section highlights. Then, in your own words, write the highlights in your ScienceLog.

• The Earth is made of three basic compositional layers—the crust, the mantle, and the core.

• The Earth is made of five main structural layers—lithosphere, asthenosphere, mesosphere, outer core, and inner core.

• Tectonic plates are large pieces of the lithosphere that move around on the Earth's surface.

• Knowledge about the structure of the Earth comes from the study of seismic waves caused by earthquakes.

SECTION 2

Vocabulary

In your own words, write a definition of each of the following terms in the space provided.

1. continental drift — theory that continents can, and have, drifted a part. Theory introduced by Alfred Wegner. Continental drift in supported by fossil evidence, glacier evidence + continent shapes.

2. sea-floor spreading — the process by which new oceanic lithosphere is created as older materials are pulled away. Mid Ocean Ridges - underwater mountain chains that run through Earths oceans Sea floor spreading occurs at mid ocean ridges.

Notes

Read the following section highlights. Then, in your own words, write the highlights in your ScienceLog.

• Wegener's theory of continental drift explained many puzzling facts, including the fit of the Atlantic coastlines of South America and Africa.

• Today's continents were originally joined together in the ancient continent Pangaea.

• Some of the most important evidence for sea-floor spreading comes from magnetic reversals recorded in the ocean floor.

Plate Tectonics, continued

SECTION 3
Vocabulary

★The San Andreas Fault in california is an exception somtimes ghifting several meters at once.

In your own words, write a definition of each of the following terms in the space provided.

1. plate tectonics — *the theory that that the Earths lithosphere is divided into tectonic plates that move around on top of the athenosphere*

2. convergent boundary — *occurs when two tectonic plates push into one another*

3. subduction zone — *The region where oceanic plates sink down into the asthenosphere*

4. divergent boundary — *two tectonic plates pull away from one another*

5. transform boundary — *two tectonic plates slide past each other horizontally*

More only a few centimeters each year

Notes

Read the following section highlights. Then, in your own words, write the highlights in your ScienceLog.

- The processes of ridge push, convection, and slab pull provide some possible driving forces for plate tectonics.
- Tectonic plate boundaries are classified as convergent, divergent, or transform.
- Data from satellite tracking indicate that some tectonic plates move an average of 3 cm a year.

When rocks change shape due to stress, it's called deformation

SECTION 4
Vocabulary

In your own words, write a definition of each of the following terms in the space provided.

1. stress — *the amount of force per unit area that is put on something*

2. compression — kind of stress that occurs when two tectonic plates colide at a convergent plate boundary

3. tension — kind of stress that occurs when something stretches. It occurs at different plate boundaries.

4. folding — deformation that occurs when rock layers bend due to stress

5. fault — occurs when rock layers break instead of bending or folding

6. normal fault — the hanging wall moves down, usually caused by tension

7. reverse fault — the hanging wall moves up, usually caused by compression

8. strike-slip fault — occurs when stress causes the two parts to slide past each other horizontally

Notes

Read the following section highlights. Then, in your own words, write the highlights in your ScienceLog.

- As tectonic plates move next to and into each other, a great amount of stress is placed on the rocks at the boundary.
- Folding occurs when rock layers bend due to stress.
- Faulting occurs when rock layers break due to stress and then move on either side of the break.
- Mountains are classified as either folded, fault-block, or volcanic, depending on how they form.
- Mountain building is caused by the movement of tectonic plates. Different types of movement cause different types of mountains.

CHAPTER

7 CHAPTER REVIEW WORKSHEET

Plate Tectonics

USING VOCABULARY

For each pair of terms, explain the difference in their meanings.

1. oceanic crust/continental crust *~Continental Crust~* *thicker than oceanic*

   composition similar to granite

   ~Oceanic Crust~ - composition similar to

   basalt, it's thinner + denser than

   continental

2. lithosphere/asthenosphere _____

   •Folded - Appalacian
   •Fault - block - Rocky
   •Volcanic - Ring of Fire -

3. convergent boundary/divergent boundary _____

4. folding/faulting _____

5. oceanic crust/oceanic lithosphere _____

Plate Tectonics, continued

6. normal fault/reverse fault _____

_____

_____

_____

_____

UNDERSTANDING CONCEPTS

Multiple Choice

7. The part of the Earth that is a liquid is the

   a. crust.
   b. mantle.
   c. outer core.
   d. inner core.

8. The part of the Earth on which the tectonic plates are able to move is the

   a. lithosphere.
   b. asthenosphere.
   c. mesosphere.
   d. subduction zone.

9. The ancient continent that contained all the landmasses is called

   a. Pangaea.
   b. Gondwana.
   c. Laurasia.
   d. Panthalassa.

10. The type of tectonic plate boundary involving a collision between two tectonic plates is

   a. divergent.
   b. transform.
   c. convergent.
   d. normal.

11. The type of tectonic plate boundary that sometimes has a subduction zone is

   a. divergent.   **c.** convergent.
   b. transform.   **d.** normal.

12. The San Andreas fault is an example of a

   a. divergent boundary.   **c.** convergent boundary.
   b. transform boundary.   **d.** normal boundary.

13. When a fold is shaped like an arch, with the fold in an upward direction, it is called a(n)

   a. monocline.   **c.** syncline.
   b. anticline.   **d.** decline.

14. The type of fault in which the hanging wall moves down relative to the footwall is called

    a. strike-slip.
    b. reverse.
    c. normal.
    d. fault block.

15. The type of mountain involving huge sections of the Earth's crust being pushed up into anticlines and synclines is the

    a. folded mountain.
    b. fault-block mountain.
    c. volcanic mountain.
    d. strike-slip mountain.

16. Continental mountain ranges are usually associated with

    a. divergent boundaries.
    b. transform boundaries.
    c. convergent boundaries.
    d. normal boundaries.

17. Mid-ocean ridges are associated with

    a. divergent boundaries.
    b. transform boundaries.
    c. convergent boundaries.
    d. normal boundaries.

Short Answer

18. What is a tectonic plate?

_____

_____

_____

19. What was the major problem with Wegener's theory of continental drift?

_____

_____

_____

20. Why is there stress on the Earth's crust?

_____

_____

_____

CHAPTER 7

CONCEPT MAPPING

21. Use the following terms to create a concept map: *sea-floor spreading, convergent boundary, divergent boundary, subduction zone, transform boundary, tectonic plates.*

CRITICAL THINKING AND PROBLEM SOLVING

Write one or two sentences to answer each of the following questions:

22. Why is it necessary to think about the different layers of the Earth in terms of both their composition and their physical properties?

_____

_____

_____

_____

Plate Tectonics, continued

23. Folded mountains usually form at the edge of a tectonic plate. How can you explain old folded mountain ranges located in the middle of a tectonic plate?

_____

_____

_____

_____

_____

_____

24. New tectonic plate material continually forms at divergent boundaries. Tectonic plate material is also continually destroyed in subduction zones at convergent boundaries. Do you think the total amount of lithosphere formed on Earth is about equal to the amount destroyed? Why?

_____

_____

_____

_____

MATH IN SCIENCE

25. Assume that a very small oceanic plate is between a mid-ocean ridge to the west and a subduction zone to the east. At the ridge, the oceanic plate is growing at a rate of 5 km every million years. At the subduction zone, the oceanic plate is being destroyed at a rate of 10 km every million years. If the oceanic plate is 100 km across, in how many million years will the oceanic plate disappear?

_____

_____

_____

_____

_____

INTERPRETING GRAPHICS

Imagine that you could travel to the center of the Earth. Use the diagram below to answer the questions that follow.

Composition	Structure
Crust (50 km)	Lithosphere (150 km)
Mantle (2,900 km)	Asthenosphere (250 km)
	Mesosphere (2,550 km)
Core (3,428 km)	Outer core (2,200 km)
	Inner core (1,228 km)

26. How far beneath Earth's surface would you have to go to find the liquid material in the Earth's core?

_____

_____

27. At what range of depth would you find mantle material but still be within the lithosphere?

_____

_____

NOW WHAT DO YOU THINK?

Take a minute to review your answers to the ScienceLog questions at the beginning of this chapter. Have your answers changed? If necessary, revise your answers based on what you have learned since you began this chapter.

CHAPTER

8 VOCABULARY & NOTES WORKSHEET

Earthquakes

By studying the Vocabulary and Notes listed for each section below, you can gain a better understanding of this chapter.

SECTION 1

Vocabulary

In your own words, write a definition of each of the following terms in the space provided.

1. seismology _the study of earthquakes_

2. fault _– break in the earth's crust along which blocks of crust slide relative to one another._

3. deformation _–the change in the shape of rock in response to stress._

4. elastic rebound _– the sudden return of elastically deformed rock to its original shape_

5. seismic waves _– waves of energy that travel through the earth_

6. P waves _– the fastest seismic wave. Referred to as primary waves_

7. S waves _– second fastest seismic waves. Referred to as secondary waves. Does most damage._
surface waves move the ground up and down in circles as the waves travel along the surface

Notes

Read the following section highlights. Then, in your own words, write the highlights in your ScienceLog.

• Earthquakes mainly occur along faults near the edges of tectonic plates.

• Elastic rebound is the direct cause of earthquakes.

• Earthquakes differ depending on what type of plate motion causes them.

• Seismic waves are classified as body waves or surface waves.

• Body waves travel through the Earth's interior, while surface waves travel along the surface.

• There are two types of body waves: P waves and S waves.

CHAPTER 8

SECTION 2

Vocabulary

In your own words, write a definition of each of the following terms in the space provided.

1. seismograph _instruments located at or near the surface of the Earth that records seismic waves._

2. seismogram _a tracing of earthquake motion created by a siesmograph._

3. epicenter _point on the Earth's surface directly above an earthquake's starting point._

4. focus _point inside the earth where the earthquake begins._

Notes

Read the following section highlights. Then, in your own words, write the highlights in your ScienceLog.

• Seismographs detect seismic waves and record them as seismograms.

• An earthquake's focus is the underground location where seismic waves begin. The earthquake's epicenter is on the surface directly above the focus.

• Seismologists use the S-P-time method to find an earthquake's epicenter.

• Seismologists use the Richter scale to measure an earthquake's strength.

SECTION 3

Vocabulary

In your own words, write a definition of each of the following terms in the space provided.

1. gap hypothesis _States that sections of active faults that have had relatively few earthquakes are likely to be the site of strong earthquakes in the future._

2. seismic gap _areas along a fault where relatively few earthquakes have occurred._

_____
Earthquakes, continued

Notes

Read the following section highlights. Then, in your own words, write the highlights in your ScienceLog.

- Earthquake hazard measures how prone an area is to experiencing earthquakes in the future.
- Some earthquake predictions are based on the relationship between earthquake strength and earthquake frequency. As earthquake frequency decreases, earthquake strength increases.
- Predictions based on the gap hypothesis target seismically inactive areas along faults for strong earthquakes in the future.
- An earthquake usually collapses a structure by displacing the structure's center of gravity off the structure's supporting base.
- Buildings and bridges can be reinforced to minimize earthquake damage.
- People in earthquake-prone areas should plan ahead for earthquakes.

SECTION 4

Vocabulary

In your own words, write a definition of each of the following terms in the space provided.

1. Moho – *a place in the Earth where the speed of seismic waves increase sharply*

_____

_____

2. shadow zone – *areas on the earth's surface where no direct seismic waves can be detected.*

_____

_____

Notes

Read the following section highlights. Then, in your own words, write the highlights in your ScienceLog.

- The Moho, shadow zone, and inner core are features discovered on and inside Earth by observing seismic waves.
- Seismology has been used to study other cosmic bodies.
- Seismic waves last much longer on the moon than they do on Earth.
- Based on early seismic studies, Mars appears much less active seismically than the Earth.
- "Sunquakes" produce energy far greater than any earthquakes we know of.

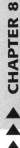

Earthquakes

USING VOCABULARY

To complete the following sentences, choose the correct term from each pair of terms listed below, and write the term in the space provided.

1. Energy is released as _____ occurs.
(deformation or elastic rebound)

2. _____ cannot travel through parts of the Earth that are completely liquid. (S waves or P waves)

3. Seismic waves are recorded by a _____.
(seismograph or seismogram)

4. Seismologists use the S-P-time method to find an earthquake's

_____. (shadow zone or epicenter)

5. The _____ is a place that marks a sharp increase in seismic wave speed. (seismic gap or Moho)

UNDERSTANDING CONCEPTS

Multiple Choice

6. When rock is _____, energy builds up in it. Seismic waves occur as this energy is

_____ .

   a. elastically deformed; released

   b. plastically deformed; released

   c. elastically deformed; increased

   d. plastically deformed; increased

7. The strongest earthquakes usually occur

   a. near divergent boundaries.

   b. near convergent boundaries.

   c. near transform boundaries.

   d. along normal faults.

8. The last seismic waves to arrive are

   a. P waves.

   b. S waves.

   c. surface waves.

   d. body waves.

9. If an earthquake begins while you are in a building, the safest thing to do first is

   a. get under the strongest table, chair, or other piece of furniture.

   b. run out into the street.

   c. crouch near a wall.

   d. call home.

_____

Earthquakes, continued

10. Studying earthquake waves currently allows seismologists to do all of the following *except*

    a. determine when an earthquake started.

    b. learn about the Earth's interior.

    c. decrease an earthquake's strength.

    d. determine where an earthquake started.

11. If a planet has a liquid core, then S waves

    a. speed up as they travel through the core.

    b. maintain their speed as they travel through the core.

    c. change direction as they travel through the core.

    d. cannot pass through the core.

Short Answer

12. What is the relationship between the strength of earthquakes and earthquake frequency?

_____

_____

_____

13. You learned earlier that if you are in a car during an earthquake and are out in the open, it is best to stay in the car. Briefly describe a situation in which you might want to leave a car during an earthquake.

_____

_____

_____

_____

14. How did scientists determine that the outer core of the Earth was liquid?

_____

_____

_____

_____

_____

_____

CHAPTER 8

CONCEPT MAPPING

15. Use the following terms to create a concept map: *focus, epicenter, earthquake start time, seismic waves, P waves, S waves.*

The Great San Fransisco Earthquake:

Wed. April 18, 1906

5:12 a.m.

More than 3000 people died, 250000 people were left homeless.

City burned for 3 days

12,000 times as powerful as the Atomic Bomb

In 3 years, the city was rebuilt.

The main post office survived- only building

6.5 billion bricks carted away.

Cost $20 million to dump mess

Greatest natural Disaster suffered by a north american city.

30x more powerful than 1989 quake

The president was Teddy Rooserelt

28000 buildings were destroyed

Impact equivalent to 6 million tons of dynamite

CRITICAL THINKING AND PROBLEM SOLVING

Write one or two sentences to answer the following questions:

16. How might the wall in Figure 2 on page 197 of your textbook appear if it had deformed elastically instead of plastically?

_____

_____

_____

_____

17. Why do strong earthquakes occur where there have not been many recent earthquakes? (Hint: Think about what gradually happens to rock before an earthquake occurs.)

_____

_____

_____

_____

_____

_____

18. What could be done to solve the wind problem with the seismograph on Mars? Explain how you would set up the seismograph.

_____

_____

_____

_____

MATH IN SCIENCE

19. Based on the relationship between earthquake magnitude and frequency, if 150 earthquakes with a magnitude of 2 occur in your area this year, about how many earthquakes with a magnitude of 4 should occur in your area this year?

_____

_____

CHAPTER 8

Name _____ Date _____ Class_____

INTERPRETING GRAPHICS

The graph below illustrates the relationship between earthquake magnitude and the height of the tracings on a seismogram. Charles Richter initially formed his magnitude scale by comparing the heights of seismogram readings for different earthquakes. Study the graph, and then answer the questions that follow.

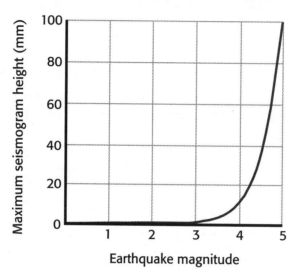

Seismogram Height vs. Earthquake Magnitude

20. What would the magnitude of an earthquake be if the height of its seismogram readings were 10 mm?

   _____

   _____

21. Look at the shape of the curve on the graph. What does this tell you about the relationship between seismogram heights and earthquake magnitudes? Explain.

   _____

   _____

   _____

   _____

NOW WHAT DO YOU THINK?

Take a minute to review your answers to the ScienceLog questions at the beginning of this chapter. Have your answers changed? If necessary, revise your answers based on what you have learned since you began this chapter.

Name _____ Date _____ Class_____

Volcanoes

By studying the Vocabulary and Notes listed for each section below, you can gain a better understanding of this chapter.

Kaitlyn

SECTION 1

Vocabulary 0.99. Cinders. large pieces of hardened magma

In your own words, write a definition of each of the following terms in the space provided.

1. volcano = a mountain that forms when molten rock (magma) is forced into the Earth's surface

1.5. vent magma rises in holes in the Earth's crust.

2. lava = magma that flows onto the earth's surface

3. pyroclastic material = consists of the rock fragments created by explosive volcano reactions.

4. volcanic dust tiny particles of hardened magma.

5. volcanic ash forced out of a volcano by rising gasses.

Notes

Read the following section highlights. Then, in your own words, write the highlights in your ScienceLog.

• Volcanoes erupt both explosively and nonexplosively.

• The characteristics of a volcanic eruption are largely determined by the type of magma within the volcano.

• The amount of silica in magma determines whether it is thin and fluid or thick and stiff. Eruptions with silica tend to be very explosive

• Lava hardens into characteristic features that range from smooth to jagged, depending on how thick the lava is and how quickly it flows.

• Pyroclastic material, or volcanic debris, consists of solid pieces of the volcano as well as magma that solidifies as it travels through the air.

• The composition of magma determines how explosive a volcano is.

• Magma with a high water content tends to erupt explosively.

SECTION 2

Vocabulary

In your own words, write a definition of each of the following terms in the space provided.

1. shield volcano — If the eruption is quiet, a gentle sloping shield volcano is produced.

2. cinder cone volcano — if the eruption is explosive, a steep sloped cinder cone volcano is produced

3. composite volcano — if the eruptions alternate between quiet and explosive a composite volcano is produced.

4. crater — funnel-shaped pit located at the top of the central vent in most volcanoes.

5. caldera — forms when a magma chamber that supplies material to a volcano empties and its roof collapses.

Volcanoes, continued

Notes

Read the following section highlights. Then, in your own words, write the highlights in your ScienceLog.

- The effects of volcanic eruptions are felt both locally and around the world.
- Volcanic mountains can be classified according to their composition and overall shape.
- Craters are funnel-shaped pits that form around the central vent of a volcano. Calderas are large bowl-shaped depressions formed by a collapsed magma chamber.
- In the largest type of volcanic eruption, lava simply pours from long fissures in the Earth's crust to form lava plateaus.

SECTION 3

a magma chamber—where magma and gasses collect between eruptions.

Vocabulary

In your own words, write a definition of each of the following terms in the space provided.

1. rift _____

_____

_____

_____

2. hot spot — *places on the earth's surface directly above colums of rising mantle plumes.*

_____

_____

Notes

3 rift—a deep crack that forms between tectonic plates as they separate

Read the following section highlights. Then, in your own words, write the highlights in your ScienceLog.

- Volcanoes result from magma formed in the mantle.
- When pressure is reduced, some of the solid rock of the already hot mantle melts to form magma.
- Because it is less dense than the surrounding rock, magma rises to the Earth's surface. It either erupts as lava or solidifies in the crust.
- Most volcanic activity takes place along tectonic plate boundaries, where plates either separate or collide.
- Volcanoes also occur at hot spots. Chains of volcanic islands can form when tectonic plates move relative to the hot spot.
- Volcanic eruptions cannot be predicted with complete accuracy. But scientists now have several methods of forecasting future eruptions.

CHAPTER 9

Name _____ Date _____ Class _____

CHAPTER

9 **CHAPTER REVIEW WORKSHEET**

Volcanoes

USING VOCABULARY

For each pair of terms, explain the difference in their meanings.

1. caldera/crater _____

• Extinct volcanoes
haven't erupted in recorded
history

• Dormant volcanoes are
2. lava/magma — not currently erupting but
have erupted at some time
in recorded history

• Active volcanoes are those
3. lava/pyroclastic material — that erupt regulary.

_____

_____

_____

_____

4. vent/rift _____

_____

_____

_____

_____

5. cinder cone volcano/shield volcano _____

_____

_____

_____

_____

Volcanoes, continued

UNDERSTANDING CONCEPTS

Multiple Choice

6. The type of magma that often produces a violent eruption can be described as

    a. thin due to high silica content.
    b. thick due to high silica content.
    c. thin due to low silica content.
    d. thick due to low silica content.

7. When lava hardens quickly to form ropy formations, it is called

    a. aa lava.
    b. pahoehoe lava.
    c. pillow lava.
    d. blocky lava.

8. Volcanic dust and ash can remain in the atmosphere for months or years, causing

    a. decreased solar reflection and higher temperatures.
    b. increased solar reflection and lower temperatures.
    c. decreased solar reflection and lower temperatures.
    d. increased solar reflection and higher temperatures.

9. Mount St. Helens, in Washington, covered the city of Spokane with tons of ash. Its eruption would most likely be described as

    a. nonexplosive, producing lava.
    b. explosive, producing lava.
    c. nonexplosive, producing pyroclastic material.
    d. explosive, producing pyroclastic material.

10. Magma forms within the mantle most often as a result of

    a. high temperature and high pressure.
    b. high temperature and low pressure.
    c. low temperature and high pressure.
    d. low temperature and low pressure.

11. At divergent plate boundaries,

    a. heat from the Earth's core produces mantle plumes.
    b. oceanic plates sink, causing magma to form.
    c. tectonic plates move apart.
    d. hot spots produce volcanoes.

12. A theory that helps to explain the causes of both earthquakes and volcanoes is the theory of

    a. subduction.
    b. plate tectonics.
    c. climatic fluctuation.
    d. mantle plumes.

▲ **CHAPTER 9**

Volcanoes, continued

Short Answer

13. Briefly describe two methods that scientists use to predict volcanic eruptions.

_____

_____

_____

_____

_____

_____

_____

14. Describe how differences in magma affect volcanic eruptions.

_____

_____

_____

_____

_____

_____

_____

15. Along what types of tectonic plate boundaries are volcanoes generally found? Why?

_____

_____

_____

_____

_____

Volcanoes, continued

16. Describe the characteristics of the three types of volcanic mountains.

_____

_____

_____

_____

_____

_____

_____

CONCEPT MAPPING

17. Use any of the terms from the vocabulary lists in Chapter Highlights to construct a concept map that illustrates the relationship between types of magma, the eruptions they produce, and the shapes of the volcanoes that result.

▲▲ CHAPTER 9

Volcanoes, continued

CRITICAL THINKING AND PROBLEM SOLVING

Write one or two sentences to answer the following questions:

18. Imagine that you are exploring a volcano that has been dormant for some time. You begin to keep notes on the types of volcanic debris you encounter as you walk. Your first notes describe volcanic ash, and later your notes describe lapilli. In what direction would you most likely be traveling—toward or away from the crater? Explain.

_____

_____

_____

_____

19. Loihi is a future Hawaiian island in the process of forming on the ocean floor. Considering how this island chain formed, tell where you think the new volcanic island will be located and why.

_____

_____

_____

_____

20. What do you think would happen to the Earth's climate if volcanic activity increased to 10 times its current level?

_____

_____

_____

_____

MATH IN SCIENCE

21. Midway Island is 1,935 km northwest of Hawaii. If the Pacific plate is moving to the northwest at 9 cm per year, how long ago was Midway Island located over the hot spot that formed it?

_____

_____

_____

INTERPRETING GRAPHICS

The following graph illustrates the average change in temperature above or below normal for a community over several years. Use the graph to answer the questions that follow.

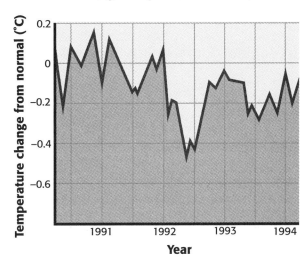

Average Temperature Variation

22. If the variation in temperature over the years was influenced by a major volcanic eruption, when did the eruption most likely take place? Explain.

_____

_____

_____

_____

23. If the temperature were plotted only in yearly intervals rather than several times per year, how might your interpretation be different?

_____

_____

_____

_____

NOW WHAT DO YOU THINK?

Take a minute to review your answers to the ScienceLog questions at the beginning of this chapter. Have your answers changed? If necessary, revise your answers based on what you have learned since you began this chapter.

CHAPTER 9

Weathering and Soil Formation

By studying the Vocabulary and Notes listed for each section below, you can gain a better understanding of this chapter.

SECTION 1

Vocabulary

In your own words, write a definition for the following terms in the space provided.

1. weathering _____

_____

2. mechanical weathering _____

3. abrasion _____

_____

4. chemical weathering _____

_____

5. acid precipitation _____

_____

6. oxidation _____

_____

Notes

Read the following section highlights. Then, in your own words, write the highlights in your ScienceLog.

- Mechanical weathering is the breakdown of rock into smaller pieces by physical means.
- Ice wedging is a process by which water flows into cracks in rock and expands as it freezes, enlarging the cracks.
- The roots of plants can grow into cracks in rocks, and the roots can enlarge the cracks as they grow.
- Gravity, water, and wind are agents of abrasion in mechanical weathering.
- The activities of plants and animals can mechanically weather rock.
- Chemical weathering is the breakdown of rock into smaller pieces by chemical means.
- Water can dissolve some rocks and minerals.
- Sulfuric and nitric acids from pollution can cause chemical weathering.
- Natural acids found in air and water and produced by plants can cause chemical weathering.

Copyright © by Holt, Rinehart and Winston. All rights reserved.

• Oxidation can cause chemical weathering when oxygen combines with iron and other metallic elements.

SECTION 2
Vocabulary

In your own words, write a definition for the following term in the space provided.

1. differential weathering _____

_____

_____

Notes

Read the following section highlights. Then, in your own words, write the highlights in your ScienceLog.

• The rate at which weathering occurs depends partly on the composition of the rock being weathered.

• The greater the surface area of a rock is, the faster the rate of weathering.

• Different climates promote different rates of weathering.

• Weathering usually occurs at a faster rate at higher elevations.

SECTION 3
Vocabulary

In your own words, write a definition for the following terms in the space provided.

1. soil _____

_____

2. bedrock _____

3. parent rock _____

4. humus _____

_____

5. topsoil _____

_____

6. leaching _____

_____

CHAPTER 10

Notes

Read the following section highlights. Then, in your own words, write the highlights in your ScienceLog.

• Soil is made up of loose, weathered material that can include organic material called humus.

• Residual soils rest on top of their parent rock, and transported soils collect in areas far from their parent rock.

• Soil usually consists of horizons, layers that are different from one another.

• Soil types vary, depending on the climate in which they form.

SECTION 4

Vocabulary

In your own words, write a definition for the following terms in the space provided.

1. soil conservation _____

_____

2. erosion _____

_____

Notes

Read the following section highlights. Then, in your own words, write the highlights in your ScienceLog.

• Soils are important because they provide nutrients for plants, homes for animals, and storage for water.

• Soils need to be protected from nutrient depletion and erosion through the use of soil conservation methods.

CHAPTER

10 CHAPTER REVIEW WORKSHEET

Weathering and Soil Formation

USING VOCABULARY

For each pair of terms, explain the difference in their meanings.

1. chemical weathering/mechanical weathering _____

_____

_____

_____

_____

_____

2. oxidation/iron oxide _____

_____

_____

_____

3. residual soil/transported soil _____

_____

_____

_____

_____

4. parent rock/bedrock _____

_____

_____

_____

5. contour plowing/terracing _____

_____

_____

_____

CHAPTER 10

Name _____ Date _____ Class_____

UNDERSTANDING CONCEPTS

Multiple Choice

6. Weathering by abrasion is usually caused by
   a. animals, plants, and wind.
   b. wind, water, and gravity.
   c. ice wedging, animals, and water.
   d. plants, gravity, and ice wedging.

7. Two acids found in acid precipitation are
   a. hydrochloric acid and sulfuric acid.
   b. nitric acid and hydrochloric acid.
   c. sulfuric acid and nitric acid.

8. Rust is produced by the oxidation of
   a. iron.   **c.** aluminum.
   b. tin.   **d.** manganese.

9. An acid normally involved in the formation of caves is
   a. nitric acid.
   b. hydrofluoric acid.
   c. hydrochloric acid.
   d. carbonic acid.

10. The soil horizon that contains humus is
   a. horizon A.   **c.** horizon C.
   b. horizon B.

11. The soil horizon that is made up of partially broken bedrock is
   a. horizon A.   **c.** horizon C.
   b. horizon B.

12. Tropical soils have the
   a. thickest horizon B.
   b. thickest horizon A.
   c. thinnest horizon A.
   d. thinnest horizon B.

13. The humus found in soils comes from
   a. parent rock.   **c.** bedrock.
   b. plants and animals.   **d.** horizon B.

14. Contour plowing means plowing
   a. up and down the slope of a hill.
   b. in steps along a hill.
   c. across the slope of a hill.
   d. in circles.

Weathering and Soil Formation, continued

15. The main reason farmers use crop rotation is to slow down the process of
   a. soil removal by wind.
   b. soil removal by water.
   c. nutrient depletion.
   d. soil compaction.

Short Answer

16. Describe the two major types of weathering.

_____

_____

_____

_____

_____

_____

17. In what type of rock do caves usually form?

_____

_____

18. Why is Devils Tower higher than the surrounding area?

_____

_____

_____

_____

19. What can happen to soil when soil conservation is not practiced?

_____

_____

_____

_____

CHAPTER 10

Weathering and Soil Formation, continued

CONCEPT MAPPING

20. Use the following terms to create a concept map: *weathering, chemical weathering, mechanical weathering, abrasion, ice wedging, oxidation, soil.*

CRITICAL THINKING AND PROBLEM SOLVING

Write one or two sentences to answer the following questions:

21. Heat generally speeds up chemical reactions. But weathering, including chemical weathering, is usually slowest in hot, dry climates. Why is this?

_____

_____

_____

_____

_____

22. How can too much rain deplete soil of its nutrients?

_____

_____

23. How does mechanical weathering speed up the effects of chemical weathering?

_____

_____

_____

MATH IN SCIENCE

24. Imagine you are a geologist working in your natural laboratory—a mountainside. You are trying to find out the speed at which ice wedging occurs. You measure several cycles of freezing and thawing in a crack in a boulder. You discover that the crack gets deeper by about 1 mm per year. The boulder is 25 cm tall. Given this rate, how long will it take for ice wedging to split this boulder in half?

_____

_____

_____

_____

CHAPTER 10

INTERPRETING GRAPHICS

The graph below shows how the density of water changes when temperature changes. The denser a substance is, the less volume it occupies. In other words, as most substances get colder, they contract and become more dense. But water is unlike most other substances—when it freezes, it expands and becomes less dense.

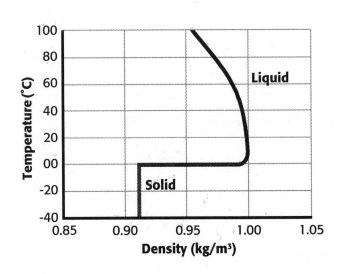

The Density of Water

25. Which will have the greater density, water at 40°C or water at –20°C?

_____

26. How would the line in the graph look different if water behaved like most other liquids?

_____

27. Which substance would be a more effective agent of mechanical weathering, water or some other liquid? Why?

_____

_____

NOW WHAT DO YOU THINK?

Take a minute to review your answers to the ScienceLog questions at the beginning of the chapter. Have your answers changed? If necessary, revise your answers based on what you have learned since you began this chapter. Record your revisions in your ScienceLog.

CHAPTER

11   VOCABULARY & NOTES WORKSHEET

The Flow of Fresh Water

By studying the Vocabulary and Notes listed for each section below, you can gain a better understanding of this chapter.

SECTION 1

Vocabulary

In your own words, write a definition of each of the following terms in the space provided.

1. erosion _____

_____

_____

2. water cycle _____

_____

_____

3. tributary _____

_____

4. drainage basin _____

_____

5. divide _____

_____

6. channel _____

_____

7. load _____

_____

Notes

Read the following section highlights. Then, in your own words, write the highlights in your ScienceLog.

- Erosion is the removal and transport of soil and rock.
- The water cycle is the continuous movement of water from water sources into the air, onto land, and back into water sources.
- A drainage basin, or watershed, includes a main river and all of its tributaries.
- The rate of stream erosion is affected by many factors, including the stream's gradient, discharge, speed, and load.
- Gradient is the change in elevation over distance.
- Discharge is the volume of water moved by a stream in a given amount of time.
- A stream's load is the material a stream can carry.
- Rivers can be described as youthful, mature, old, or rejuvenated.

SECTION 2

Vocabulary

In your own words, write a definition of each of the following terms in the space provided.

1. deposition _____

_____

2. alluvium _____

_____

3. delta _____

_____

_____

4. alluvial fan _____

_____

5. flood plain _____

_____

Notes

Read the following section highlights. Then, in your own words, write the highlights in your ScienceLog.

- Deposition occurs when eroded soil and rock are dropped.
- Alluvium is the material deposited by rivers and streams.

The Flow of Fresh Water, continued

- Deltas are deposits of alluvium at a river's mouth.
- Alluvial fans are deposits of alluvium at the base of a mountain.
- Flood plains are rich farming areas because flooding brings new soils to the area.

SECTION 3

Vocabulary

In your own words, write a definition of each of the following terms in the space provided.

1. ground water _____

_____

_____

2. water table _____

_____

_____

3. aquifer _____

_____

_____

4. porosity _____

_____

_____

5. permeability _____

_____

_____

6. recharge zone _____

_____

_____

7. artesian spring _____

_____

_____

Notes

Read the following section highlights. Then, in your own words, write the highlights in your ScienceLog.

- Ground water is located below the Earth's surface.
- Ground water can dissolve rock, especially limestone.
- The zone of aeration and the zone of saturation meet at a boundary called the water table.
- An aquifer is a porous and permeable rock layer through which ground water flows.
- A sinkhole forms when the water table is lower than the roof of an underground cave.

SECTION 4

Vocabulary

In your own words, write a definition of each of the following terms in the space provided.

1. point-source pollution _____

_____

_____

2. nonpoint-source pollution _____

_____

_____

3. sewage treatment plant _____

_____

_____

4. septic tank _____

_____

_____

Notes

Read the following section highlights. Then, in your own words, write the highlights in your ScienceLog.

- Sewage is treated in sewage treatment plants and in septic tanks.
- In a sewage treatment plant, water is cleaned in two different ways—primary treatment and secondary treatment.
- While water is generally considered to be a renewable resource, when overused it can sometimes be categorized as a nonrenewable resource.

Name _____ Date _____ Class _____

The Flow of Fresh Water

USING VOCABULARY

For each set of terms, identify the term that doesn't belong, and explain why.

1. tributary/river/water table _____

_____

_____

_____

2. load/discharge/aquifer _____

_____

_____

_____

3. delta/alluvial fan/divide _____

_____

_____

_____

4. porosity/permeability/deposition _____

_____

_____

_____

5. point-source pollution/nonpoint-source pollution/septic tank _____

_____

_____

_____

6. primary treatment/secondary treatment/drainage basin _____

_____

_____

_____

UNDERSTANDING CONCEPTS

Multiple Choice

7. Which of the following processes is NOT part of the water cycle?

    a. evaporation   **c.** condensation

    b. infiltration   **d.** deposition

8. Which type of stream load makes a river look muddy?

    a. bed load   **c.** suspended load

    b. dissolved load   **d.** gravelly load

9. What features are common in youthful river channels?

    a. meanders   **c.** rapids

    b. flood plains   **d.** sandbars

10. Which depositional feature is found at the coast?

    a. delta   **c.** alluvial fan

    b. flood plain   **d.** placer deposit

11. Caves are mainly a product of

    a. erosion by rivers.   **c.** water pollution.

    b. river deposition.   **d.** erosion by ground water.

12. The largest drainage basin in the United States is the

    a. Amazon.   **c.** Colorado.

    b. Columbia.   **d.** Mississippi.

13. An aquifer must be

    a. nonporous and nonpermeable.

    b. nonporous and permeable.

    c. porous and nonpermeable.

    d. porous and permeable.

14. Which of the following is a point source of water pollution?

    a. fertilizer from a farming area

    b. runoff from city streets

    c. a wastewater pipe

    d. leaking septic tanks

15. During primary treatment at a sewage treatment plant,

    a. water is sent to an aeration tank.

    b. water is mixed with bacteria and oxygen.

    c. dirty water is passed through a large screen.

    d. water is sent to a settling tank where chlorine is added.

Short Answer

16. What is the relationship between tributaries and rivers?

_____

_____

17. How are aquifers replenished?

_____

_____

_____

18. Why are caves usually found in limestone-rich regions?

_____

_____

_____

CONCEPT MAPPING

19. Use the following terms to create a concept map: *zone of aeration, zone of saturation, water table, gravity, porosity, permeability.*

CRITICAL THINKING AND PROBLEM SOLVING

Write one or two sentences to answer the following questions:

20. What role does water play in erosion and deposition?

_____

_____

_____

_____

21. What are the features of a river channel that has a steep gradient?

_____

_____

_____

_____

22. Why is ground water hard to clean up?

_____

_____

_____

_____

_____

_____

_____

23. Imagine you are hiking beside a mature stream. What would the stream be like?

_____

_____

_____

_____

_____

24. How can water be considered both a renewable and a nonrenewable resource? Give an example of each case.

_____

_____

_____

_____

_____

MATH IN SCIENCE

25. A sinkhole has formed in a town with a population of 5,000. The town is declared a disaster area, and $2 million is given to the town by the federal government. The local government uses 60 percent of the money for repairs to city property, and the rest is given to the townspeople.

a. How much would each person receive?

_____

b. If there are 2,000 families in the town, how much would each family receive?

_____

c. Would each family receive enough money to help them rebuild a home? If not, how could the money be distributed more fairly?

_____

_____

_____

_____

The Flow of Fresh Water, continued

INTERPRETING GRAPHICS

The hydrograph below illustrates river flow over a period of 1 year. The discharge readings are from the Yakima River, in Washington. The Yakima River flows eastward from the Cascade Mountains to the Columbia River. Study the graph, and then answer the questions that follow.

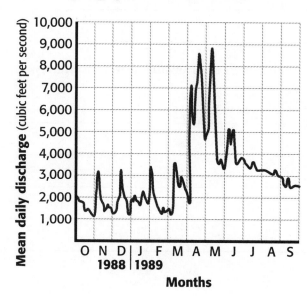

Hydrograph of the Yakima River

26. In which months is there the highest river discharge?

_____

_____

27. Why is there such a high river discharge during these months?

_____

_____

28. What might cause the peaks in river discharge between November and March?

_____

_____

NOW WHAT DO YOU THINK?

Take a minute to review your answers to the ScienceLog questions at the beginning of this chapter. Have your answers changed? If necessary, revise your answers based on what you have learned since you began this chapter.

12 VOCABULARY & NOTES WORKSHEET

Agents of Erosion and Deposition

By studying the Vocabulary and Notes listed for each section below, you can gain a better understanding of this chapter.

SECTION 1
Vocabulary
In your own words, write a definition of each of the following terms in the space provided.

1. shoreline _____

_____

2. beach _____

_____

3. longshore current _____

_____

Notes
Read the following section highlights. Then, in your own words, write the highlights in your ScienceLog.
- The wind from storms usually produces the large waves that cause shoreline erosion.
- Waves break when they enter shallow water, becoming surf.
- Beaches are made of any material deposited by waves.
- Sandbars and spits are depositional features caused by longshore currents.
- Sea cliffs, sea caves, sea arches, and sea stacks are coastal formations caused by wave erosion.

SECTION 2
Vocabulary
In your own words, write a definition of each of the following terms in the space provided.

1. saltation _____

_____

_____

2. deflation _____

_____

_____

3. abrasion _____

_____

4. dune _____

_____

5. loess _____

_____

Notes

Read the following section highlights. Then, in your own words, write the highlights in your ScienceLog.

- Wind is an important agent of erosion and deposition in deserts and along coastlines.
- Saltation is the process of the wind bouncing sand grains downwind along the ground.
- Deflation is the removal of materials by wind. If deflation removes all fine rock materials, a barren surface called desert pavement is formed.
- Abrasion is the grinding and wearing down of rock surfaces by other rock or sand particles.
- Dunes are formations caused by wind-deposited sand.
- Loess is wind-deposited silt, and it forms soil material good for farming.

SECTION 3

Vocabulary

In your own words, write a definition of each of the following terms in the space provided.

1. glacier _____

_____

2. iceberg _____

_____

3. crevasse _____

_____

4. glacial drift _____

_____

_____

5. stratified drift _____

_____

_____

6. till _____

_____

_____

Notes

Read the following section highlights. Then, in your own words, write the highlights in your ScienceLog.

• Masses of moving ice are called glaciers.

• There are two main types of glaciers—alpine glaciers and continental glaciers.

• Glaciers move when the ice that comes into contact with the ground melts and when ice crystals slip over one another.

• Alpine glaciers produce rugged landscape features, such as cirques, arêtes, and horns.

• Continental glaciers smooth the landscape.

• There are two main types of glacial deposits—stratified drift and till.

• Some of the landforms deposited by glaciers include outwash plains, eskers, and moraines.

SECTION 4

Vocabulary

In your own words, write a definition of each of the following terms in the space provided.

1. mass movement _____

_____

_____

_____

2. rock fall _____

_____

_____

_____

3. landslide _____

_____

_____

_____

4. mudflow _____

_____

_____

_____

5. creep _____

_____

_____

Notes

Read the following section highlights. Then, in your own words, write the highlights in your ScienceLog.

- Mass movement is the movement of material downhill due to the force of gravity.
- The angle of repose is the steepest slope at which loose material will remain at rest.
- Rock falls, landslides, and mudflows are all types of rapid mass movement.
- Creep is a type of slow mass movement.

CHAPTER

12 CHAPTER REVIEW WORKSHEET

Agents of Erosion and Deposition

USING VOCABULARY

For each pair of terms, explain the difference in their meanings.

1. shoreline/longshore current _____

_____

_____

_____

2. beaches/dunes _____

_____

_____

_____

3. deflation/saltation _____

_____

_____

_____

4. glacier/loess _____

_____

_____

_____

5. stratified drift/till _____

_____

_____

_____

6. mudflow/creep _____

_____

_____

_____

Agents of Erosion and Deposition, continued

UNDERSTANDING CONCEPTS

Multiple Choice

7. *Surf* refers to

    a. large storm waves in the open ocean.

    b. giant waves produced by hurricanes.

    c. breaking waves.

    d. small waves on a calm sea.

8. When waves cut completely through a headland, a _____ is formed.

    a. sea cave   **c.** sea stack

    b. sea cliff   **d.** sea arch

9. A narrow strip of sand that is formed by wave deposition and is connected to the shore is called a

    a. marine terrace.   **c.** spit.

    b. sandbar.   **d.** headland.

10. A wind-eroded depression is called a

    a. dune.   **c.** deflation hollow.

    b. desert pavement.   **d.** dust bowl.

11. Where is the world's largest ice sheet located?

    a. Greenland

    b. Canada

    c. Alaska

    d. Antarctica

12. The process of calving forms

    a. continental ice sheets.

    b. icebergs.

    c. U-shaped valleys.

    d. moraines.

13. What term describes all types of glacial deposits?

    a. drift   **c.** till

    b. loess   **d.** outwash

14. Which of the following is not a landform created by an alpine glacier?

    a. cirque   **c.** horn

    b. deflation hollow   **d.** arête

15. What is the term for a mass movement of volcanic origin?

    a. lahar   **c.** creep

    b. slump   **d.** rock fall

16. Which of the following is a slow mass movement?

    a. mudflow   **c.** creep

    b. landslide   **d.** rock fall

Short Answer

17. Why do waves break when they get near the shore?

_____

_____

_____

_____

_____

18. What role do storms play in coastal erosion?

_____

_____

_____

_____

19. How do humans increase the erosion caused by dust storms?

_____

_____

_____

_____

_____

20. In what direction do sand dunes move?

_____

_____

_____

21. Why are glaciers such effective agents of erosion and deposition?

_____

_____

_____

CHAPTER 12

22. List some evidence for creep.

_____

_____

CONCEPT MAPPING

23. Use the following terms to create a concept map: *deflation, dust storm, saltation, dune, loess.*

CRITICAL THINKING AND PROBLEM SOLVING

Write one or two sentences to answer the following questions:

24. What role does wind play in the processes of erosion and deposition?

_____

_____

_____

_____

Agents of Erosion and Deposition, continued

25. What are the main differences between alpine glaciers and continental glaciers?

_____

_____

_____

_____

_____

_____

26. Describe the different types of moraines.

_____

_____

_____

_____

_____

27. What kind of mass movement occurs continuously, day after day? Why can't you see it?

_____

_____

_____

_____

MATH IN SCIENCE

28. While standing on a beach, you can estimate a wave's speed in kilometers per hour. This is done by counting the seconds between each arriving wave crest to determine the wave period and then multiplying the wave period by 3.5. Calculate the speed of a wave with a 10-second period.

_____

_____

_____

Agents of Erosion and Deposition, continued

INTERPRETING GRAPHICS

The following graph illustrates coastal erosion and deposition occurring at an imaginary beach over a period of 8 years. Use the graph to answer the questions that follow.

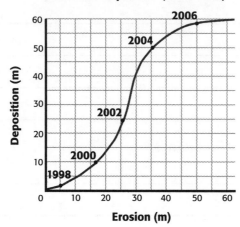

Erosion and Deposition (1998–2006)

29. What is happening to the beach over time?

_____

_____

_____

30. In what year does the amount of erosion that has occurred along the shoreline equal the amount of deposition?

_____

31. Based on the erosion and deposition data for 2000, what might happen to the beach in the years to follow?

_____

_____

_____

_____

_____

NOW WHAT DO YOU THINK?

Take a minute to review your answers to the ScienceLog questions at the beginning of this chapter. Have your answers changed? If necessary, revise your answers based on what you have learned since you began this chapter.

CHAPTER

13 VOCABULARY & NOTES WORKSHEET

Exploring the Oceans

By studying the Vocabulary and Notes listed for each section below, you can gain a better understanding of this chapter.

SECTION 1

Vocabulary

In your own words, write a definition of each of the following terms in the space provided.

1. salinity _____

_____

_____

2. thermocline _____

_____

_____

3. water cycle _____

_____

_____

Notes

Read the following section highlights. Then, in your own words, write the highlights in your ScienceLog.

• The four oceans as we know them today formed within the last 300 million years.

• Salts have been added to the ocean for billions of years.

• The three temperature zones of ocean water are the surface zone, thermocline, and deep zone.

• The ocean plays the largest role in the water cycle.

• The ocean stabilizes Earth's conditions by absorbing and retaining heat.

SECTION 2

Vocabulary

In your own words, write a definition of each of the following terms in the space provided.

1. continental shelf _____

_____

_____

2. continental slope _____

_____

_____

3. continental rise _____

_____

_____

4. abyssal plain _____

_____

_____

5. mid-ocean ridge _____

_____

_____

6. rift valley _____

_____

7. seamount _____

_____

_____

8. ocean trench _____

_____

_____

Notes

Read the following section highlights. Then, in your own words, write the highlights in your ScienceLog.

- The ocean floor is divided into zones based on depth and slope.
- The continental margin consists of the continental shelf, the continental slope, and the continental rise.
- The deep-ocean basin consists of the abyssal plain, with features such as mid-ocean ridges, rift valleys, seamounts, and ocean trenches.
- In addition to directly studying the ocean floor, scientists indirectly study the ocean floor using sonar and satellites.

SECTION 3
Vocabulary
In your own words, write a definition of each of the following terms in the space provided.

1. plankton _____

_____

_____

_____

2. nekton _____

_____

_____

_____

3. benthos _____

_____

_____

4. benthic environment _____

_____

_____

_____

5. pelagic environment _____

_____

_____

_____

Notes
Read the following section highlights. Then, in your own words, write the highlights in your ScienceLog.

- There are three main groups of marine life—plankton, nekton, and benthos.
- The two main ocean environments—the benthic and pelagic environments—are divided into ecological zones based on the locations of organisms that live in the environments.

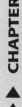

▲ CHAPTER 13

SECTION 4

Vocabulary

In your own words, write a definition of the following term in the space provided.

1. desalination _____

_____

_____

_____

_____

Notes

Read the following section highlights. Then, in your own words, write the highlights in your ScienceLog.

• Humans depend on the ocean for living and nonliving resources.

• Ocean farms raise fish and other marine life to help feed growing human populations.

• Nonliving ocean resources include oil and natural gas, fresh water, minerals, and tidal and wave energy.

SECTION 5

Vocabulary

In your own words, write a definition of the following term in the space provided.

1. nonpoint-source pollution _____

_____

_____

_____

_____

Notes

Read the following section highlights. Then, in your own words, write the highlights in your ScienceLog.

• Types of ocean pollution include trash dumping, sludge dumping, nonpoint-source pollution, and oil spills.

• Nonpoint-source pollution cannot be traced to specific points of origin.

• Efforts to save ocean resources include international treaties and volunteer cleanups.

CHAPTER

13 CHAPTER REVIEW WORKSHEET

Exploring the Oceans

USING VOCABULARY

To complete the following sentences, choose the correct term from each pair of terms listed below, and write the term in the space provided.

1. The region of the ocean floor that is closest to the shoreline is the

_____. (continental shelf or continental slope)

2. Below the surface layer of the ocean is a layer of water that gets colder with depth and

extends to a depth of 700 m. This layer is called the _____.
(thermocline or benthic environment)

3. _____ typically float at or near the ocean's surface.
(Plankton or Nekton)

Correct the wrong terminology in each of the following sentences. A word bank is below. Rewrite the sentences with the correct terminology in the space provided.

4. The water cycle is the process of evaporating sea water so that the water and salt separate.

_____

_____

_____

5. Types of nekton include sea stars and clams.

_____

_____

_____

Word bank: nonpoint-source pollution, plankton, desalination, benthos

For each pair of terms, explain the difference in their meanings.

6. ocean trench/rift valley _____

_____

_____

_____

_____

▲▲ CHAPTER 13
▲▲
▲

7. salinity/desalination _____

_____

_____

_____

8. nekton/benthos _____

_____

_____

9. pelagic environment/benthic environment _____

_____

_____

_____

UNDERSTANDING CONCEPTS

Multiple Choice

10. The largest ocean is the
   a. Indian Ocean.
   b. Pacific Ocean.
   c. Atlantic Ocean.
   d. Arctic Ocean.

11. One of the most abundant elements in the ocean is
   a. potassium.
   b. calcium.
   c. chlorine.
   d. magnesium.

12. Which of the following affects the ocean's salinity?
   a. fresh water added by rivers
   b. currents
   c. evaporation
   d. All of the above

13. Most precipitation falls
   a. on land.
   b. into lakes and rivers.
   c. into the ocean.
   d. in rain forests.

14. Which benthic zone has a depth range between 200 m and 4,000 m?
   a. bathyal zone
   b. abyssal zone
   c. hadal zone
   d. sublittoral zone

15. The ocean floor and all the organisms that live on it or in it is the
   a. benthic environment.
   b. pelagic environment.
   c. neritic zone.
   d. oceanic zone.

Short Answer

16. Why does coastal water in areas with hotter, drier climates typically have a higher salinity than coastal water in cooler, more humid areas?

_____

_____

_____

17. What is the difference between the abyssal plain and the abyssal zone?

_____

_____

_____

18. How do the continental shelf, the continental slope, the continental rise, and the continental margin relate to each other?

_____

_____

_____

CONCEPT MAPPING

19. Use the following terms to create a concept map: *marine life, plankton, nekton, benthos, benthic environment, pelagic environment.*

CHAPTER 13 ▲▲▲

CRITICAL THINKING AND PROBLEM SOLVING

Write one or two sentences to answer the following questions:

20. Other than obtaining fresh water, what benefit comes from desalination?

_____

_____

_____

_____

_____

21. Explain the difference between a bathymetric profile and a seismic reading.

_____

_____

_____

_____

_____

_____

MATH IN SCIENCE

22. Imagine that you are in the kelp-farming business and that your kelp grows 33 cm per day. You begin harvesting when your plants are 50 cm tall. During the first seven days of harvest, you cut 10 cm off the top of your kelp plants each day. How tall would your kelp plants be after the seventh day of harvesting?

_____

_____

_____

Name _____ Date _____ Class_____

INTERPRETING GRAPHICS

Examine the image below, and answer the questions that follow.

Ecological Zones of the Ocean

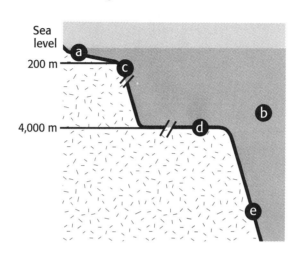

23. At which point (a, b, c, d, or e) would you most likely find an anglerfish?

_____

24. At which point would you most likely find tube worms?

_____

25. Which ecological zone is at point c?

_____

_____

Which depth zone is at point c?

_____

_____

26. Name a type of organism you might find at point e.

_____

_____

NOW WHAT DO YOU THINK?

Take a minute to review your answers to the ScienceLog questions at the beginning of this chapter. Have your answers changed? If necessary, revise your answers based on what you have learned since you began this chapter.

▲ CHAPTER 13

The Movement of Ocean Water

By studying the Vocabulary and Notes listed for each section below, you can gain a better understanding of this chapter.

SECTION 1

Vocabulary

In your own words, write a definition of each of the following terms in the space provided.

1. surface current _____

_____

_____

2. Coriolis effect _____

_____

_____

3. deep current _____

_____

4. upwelling _____

_____

_____

5. El Niño _____

_____

_____

Notes

Read the following section highlights. Then, in your own words, write the highlights in your ScienceLog.

- Currents are classified as surface currents and deep currents.
- Surface currents are controlled by three factors: global winds, the Coriolis effect, and continental deflections.
- Surface currents, such as the Gulf Stream, can be several thousand kilometers in length.
- Deep currents form where the density of ocean water increases. Water density depends on temperature and salinity.
- Surface currents affect the climate of the land near which they flow.

The Movement of Ocean Water, continued

SECTION 2
Vocabulary
In your own words, write a definition of each of the following terms in the space provided.

1. crest _____

_____

_____

2. trough _____

_____

_____

3. wavelength _____

_____

_____

4. wave height _____

_____

_____

5. wave period _____

_____

_____

6. breaker _____

_____

_____

7. surf _____

_____

_____

8. whitecap _____

_____

_____

▲ CHAPTER 14

9. swells _____

_____

_____

10. tsunami _____

_____

_____

_____

11. storm surge _____

_____

_____

_____

Notes

Read the following section highlights. Then, in your own words, write the highlights in your ScienceLog.

- Waves are made up of two main components—crests and troughs.
- Waves are usually created by the transfer of the wind's energy across the surface of the ocean.
- Waves travel through water near the water's surface, while the water itself rises and falls in circular movements.
- Waves travel in the direction the wind blows. If the wind blows over a long distance, the wavelength becomes very large and the waves travel quickly.
- Wind-generated waves are classified as deep-water and shallow-water waves.
- Tsunamis are dangerous waves that can be very destructive to coastal communities.

SECTION 3

Vocabulary

In your own words, write a definition of each of the following terms in the space provided.

1. tides _____

_____

_____

_____

The Movement of Ocean Water, continued

2. tidal range _____

_____

_____

_____

_____

3. spring tides _____

_____

_____

_____

_____

4. neap tides _____

_____

_____

_____

_____

Notes

Read the following section highlights. Then, in your own words, write the highlights in your ScienceLog.

- Tides are caused by the gravitational forces of the moon and sun tugging on the Earth.
- The moon's gravity is the main force behind tides.
- The relative positions of the sun and moon with respect to Earth cause different tidal ranges.
- Maximum tidal range occurs during spring tides.
- Minimum tidal range occurs during neap tides.
- Tidal bores occur as high tide rises in narrow coastal inlets.

CHAPTER 14

The Movement of Ocean Water

USING VOCABULARY

For each pair of terms, explain the difference in their meanings.

1. wavelength/wave height _____

_____

_____

_____

2. whitecap/swell _____

_____

_____

_____

3. tsunami/storm surge _____

_____

_____

_____

4. spring tide/neap tide _____

_____

_____

_____

Correct the wrong terminology in each of the following sentences. A word bank is below. Rewrite the sentences with the correct terminology in the space provided.

5. Deep currents are directly controlled by wind.

_____

_____

_____

_____

The Movement of Ocean Water, continued

_____

6. The Coriolis effect reduces upwelling along the coast of South America.

_____

_____

_____

_____

7. Neap tides occur when the moon is between the Earth and the sun.

_____

_____

_____

8. A tidal bore is the difference between levels of ocean water at high tide and low tide.

_____

_____

_____

_____

Word bank: breakers, spring tides, tsunamis, surface currents, tidal range, El Niño

UNDERSTANDING CONCEPTS

Multiple Choice

9. Surface currents are formed by
- **a.** the moon's gravity.
- **b.** the sun's gravity.
- **c.** wind.
- **d.** increased water density.

10. Deep currents form when
- **a.** cold air decreases water density.
- **b.** warm air increases water density.
- **c.** the ocean surface freezes and solids from the water underneath are removed.
- **d.** salinity increases.

11. When waves come near the shore,
- **a.** they speed up.
- **b.** they maintain their speed.
- **c.** their wavelength increases.
- **d.** their wave height increases.

CHAPTER 14

12. Longshore currents transport sediment

   a. out to the open ocean.
   b. along the shore.
   c. during low tide only.
   d. during high tide only.

13. Whitecaps break

   a. in the surf.
   b. in the breaker zone.
   c. in the open ocean.
   d. as their wavelength increases.

14. Tidal range is greatest during

   a. spring tide.
   b. neap tide.
   c. a tidal bore.
   d. the day only.

Short Answer

15. Explain the relationship between upwelling and El Niño.

_____

_____

_____

_____

_____

_____

16. Explain what happens when the North Atlantic Deep Water meets the Antarctic Bottom Water.

_____

_____

_____

_____

_____

_____

The Movement of Ocean Water, continued

17. Describe the relative positions of the Earth, the moon, and the sun during neap tide. Where do high tide and low tide occur during this time? Include a sketch to illustrate their positions.

_____

_____

_____

_____

_____

_____

18. Explain the difference between the breaker zone and the surf.

_____

_____

_____

_____

CONCEPT MAPPING

19. Use the following terms to create a concept map: *wind, deep currents, sun's gravity, types of ocean-water movement, surface currents, tides, increasing water density, waves, moon's gravity.*

CRITICAL THINKING AND PROBLEM SOLVING

Write one or two sentences to answer the following questions:

20. What would happen to surface currents if the Earth reversed its rotation? Be specific.

_____
_____
_____

21. How would you explain a bottle moving across the water in the same direction the waves are traveling?

_____
_____

22. You and a friend are planning a fishing trip to the ocean. Your friend tells you that the fish bite more in his secret fishing spot during low tide. If low tide occurred at the spot at 7 A.M. today and you are going to fish there in one week, at what time will low tide occur in that spot?

_____

The Movement of Ocean Water, continued

MATH IN SCIENCE

23. If a barrier island that is 1 km wide and 10 km long loses 1.5 m of its width per year to erosion by longshore current, how long will it take for the island to lose one-fourth of its width?

_____

_____

INTERPRETING GRAPHICS

Study the diagram on page 385 of your textbook, and answer the questions that follow.

24. At which position (A, B, C, or D) would the moon be during a neap tide?

_____

25. At which position (A, B, C, or D) would the moon be during a spring tide?

_____

26. Would the tidal range be greater with the moon at position C or position D? Why?

_____

_____

_____

_____

_____

NOW WHAT DO YOU THINK?

Take a minute to review your answers to the ScienceLog questions at the beginning of this chapter. Have your answers changed? If necessary, revise your answers based on what you have learned since you began this chapter.

CHAPTER 14

CHAPTER
15 VOCABULARY & NOTES WORKSHEET

The Atmosphere

By studying the Vocabulary and Notes listed for each section below, you can gain a better understanding of this chapter.

SECTION 1

Vocabulary

In your own words, write a definition of each of the following terms in the space provided.

1. atmosphere _____

_____

2. air pressure _____

_____

_____

3. altitude _____

_____

4. troposphere _____

_____

5. stratosphere _____

_____

6. ozone _____

_____

_____

7. mesosphere _____

_____

8. thermosphere _____

_____

Notes

Read the following section highlights. Then, in your own words, write the highlights in your ScienceLog.

• The atmosphere is a mixture of gases.

• Nitrogen and oxygen are the two most abundant atmospheric gases.

The Atmosphere, continued

- Throughout the atmosphere, there are changes in air pressure, temperature, and gases.
- Air pressure decreases as altitude increases.
- Temperature differences in the atmosphere are a result of the way solar energy is absorbed as it moves downward through the atmosphere.
- The troposphere is the lowest and densest layer of the atmosphere. All weather occurs in the troposphere.
- The stratosphere contains the ozone layer, which protects us from harmful radiation.
- The mesosphere is the coldest layer of the atmosphere.
- The uppermost atmospheric layer is the thermosphere.

SECTION 2

Vocabulary

In your own words, write a definition of each of the following terms in the space provided.

1. radiation _____

_____

2. conduction _____

_____

3. convection _____

_____

_____

4. greenhouse effect _____

_____

_____

5. global warming _____

_____

Notes

Read the following section highlights. Then, in your own words, write the highlights in your ScienceLog.

- The Earth receives energy from the sun in the form of radiation.
- Radiation that reaches the Earth's surface is absorbed or reflected.
- Heat is transferred through the atmosphere by conduction and convection.
- The greenhouse effect is caused by gases in the atmosphere that trap heat that is reflected off and radiated from the Earth's surface.

CHAPTER 15

SECTION 3

Vocabulary

In your own words, write a definition of each of the following terms in the space provided.

1. wind _____

_____

_____

2. Coriolis effect _____

_____

_____

3. trade winds _____

_____

_____

4. westerlies _____

_____

_____

5. polar easterlies _____

_____

_____

6. jet streams _____

_____

_____

Notes

Read the following section highlights. Then, in your own words, write the highlights in your ScienceLog.

- At the Earth's surface, winds blow from areas of high pressure to areas of low pressure.
- Pressure belts exist approximately every 30° of latitude.
- The Coriolis effect makes wind curve as it moves across the Earth's surface.
- Global winds are part of a pattern of air circulation across the Earth and include the trade winds, the westerlies, and the polar easterlies.
- Local winds move short distances, can blow in any direction, and are influenced by geography.

SECTION 4

Vocabulary

In your own words, write a definition of each of the following terms in the space provided.

1. primary pollutants _____

_____

_____

_____

_____

2. secondary pollutants _____

_____

_____

_____

_____

3. acid precipitation _____

_____

_____

_____

_____

Notes

Read the following section highlights. Then, in your own words, write the highlights in your ScienceLog.

• Air pollutants are generally classified as primary or secondary pollutants.

• Human-caused pollution comes from a variety of sources, including factories, cars, and homes.

• Air pollution can heighten problems associated with allergies, lung problems, and heart problems.

• The Clean Air Act has reduced air pollution by controlling the amount of pollutants that can be released from cars and factories.

CHAPTER

15 CHAPTER REVIEW WORKSHEET

The Atmosphere

USING VOCABULARY

For each pair of terms, explain the difference in their meanings.

1. air pressure/altitude _____

_____

_____

_____

2. troposphere/thermosphere _____

_____

_____

_____

3. greenhouse effect/global warming _____

_____

_____

_____

4. convection/conduction _____

_____

_____

_____

5. global wind/local wind _____

_____

_____

6. primary pollutant/secondary pollutant _____

_____

_____

_____

_____

_____

_____

UNDERSTANDING CONCEPTS

Multiple Choice

7. What is the most abundant gas in the air that we breathe?

  a. oxygen   **c.** hydrogen

  b. nitrogen   **d.** carbon dioxide

8. The major source of oxygen for the Earth's atmosphere is

  a. sea water.   **c.** plants.

  b. the sun.   **d.** animals.

9. The bottom layer of the atmosphere, where almost all weather occurs, is the

  a. stratosphere.   **c.** thermosphere.

  b. troposphere.   **d.** mesosphere.

10. About _____ percent of the solar radiation that reaches the outer atmosphere is absorbed at the Earth's surface.

  a. 20   **c.** 50

  b. 30   **d.** 70

11. The ozone layer is located in the

  a. stratosphere.

  b. troposphere.

  c. thermosphere.

  d. mesosphere.

12. How does most heat energy in the atmosphere move?

  a. conduction

  b. convection

  c. advection

  d. radiation

13. The balance between incoming radiation and outgoing heat energy is called

  a. convection.

  b. conduction.

  c. greenhouse effect.

  d. radiation balance.

_____

The Atmosphere, continued

14. Most of the United States is located in which prevailing wind belt?

    a. westerlies   **c.** southeast trade winds

    b. northeast trade winds   **d.** doldrums

15. Which of the following is NOT a primary pollutant?

    a. car exhaust

    b. acid precipitation

    c. smoke from a factory

    d. fumes from burning plastic

16. The Clean Air Act

    a. controls the amount of air pollutants that can be released from most sources.

    b. requires cars to run on fuels other than gasoline.

    c. requires many industries to use scrubbers.

    d. (a) and (c) only

Short Answer

17. Why does the atmosphere become less dense as altitude increases?

_____

_____

_____

_____

18. Explain why air rises when it is heated.

_____

_____

_____

_____

19. What causes temperature changes in the atmosphere?

_____

_____

_____

_____

_____

20. What are secondary pollutants, and how are they formed? Give an example.

_____

_____

_____

_____

CONCEPT MAPPING

21. Use the following terms to create a concept map: *altitude, air pressure, temperature, atmosphere.*

CRITICAL THINKING AND PROBLEM SOLVING

Write one or two sentences to answer the following questions:

22. What is the relationship between the greenhouse effect and global warming?

_____

_____

_____

_____

_____

23. How do you think the Coriolis effect would change if the Earth were to rotate twice as fast? Explain.

_____

_____

_____

_____

_____

24. Without the atmosphere, the Earth's surface would be very different. What are several ways that the atmosphere affects the Earth?

_____

_____

_____

_____

_____

_____

Name _____ Date _____ Class _____

MATH IN SCIENCE

25. Wind speed is measured in miles per hour and in knots. One mile (statute mile or land mile) is 5,280 ft. One nautical mile (or sea mile) is 6,076 ft. Speed in nautical miles is measured in knots. Calculate the wind speed in knots if the wind is blowing at 25 mi/h.

INTERPRETING GRAPHICS

Use the wind-chill chart to answer the questions that follow.

Wind-Chill Chart

Wind Speed		Actual thermometer reading (°F)				
		40	30	20	10	0
Knots	mph	Equivalent temperature (°F)				
Calm		40	30	20	10	0
4	5	37	27	16	6	–5
9	10	28	16	4	–9	–21
13	15	22	9	–5	–18	–36
17	20	18	4	–10	–25	–39
22	25	16	0	–15	–29	–44
26	30	13	–2	–18	–33	–48
30	35	11	–4	–20	–35	–49

26. If the wind speed is 20 mi/h and the temperature is 40°F, how cold will the air seem?

27. If the wind speed is 30 mi/h and the temperature is 20°F, how cold will the air seem?

NOW WHAT DO YOU THINK?

Take a minute to review your answers to the ScienceLog questions at the beginning of this chapter. Have your answers changed? If necessary, revise your answers based on what you have learned since you began this chapter.

CHAPTER 15

CHAPTER

16 VOCABULARY & NOTES WORKSHEET

Understanding Weather

By studying the Vocabulary and Notes listed for each section below, you can gain a better understanding of this chapter.

SECTION 1

Vocabulary

In your own words, write a definition of each of the following terms in the space provided.

1. weather _____

_____

_____

2. water cycle _____

_____

_____

_____

3. humidity _____

_____

4. relative humidity _____

_____

_____

5. condensation _____

_____

6. dew point _____

_____

_____

7. cloud _____

_____

_____

8. precipitation _____

_____

Notes

Read the following section highlights. Then, in your own words, write the highlights in your ScienceLog.

• Water is continuously moving and changing state as it moves through the water cycle.

• Humidity is the amount of water vapor or moisture in the air. Relative humidity is the amount of moisture the air contains compared with the maximum amount it can hold at a particular temperature.

• Water droplets form because of condensation.

• Dew point is the temperature at which air must cool to be saturated.

• Condensation occurs when the air next to a surface cools to below its dew point.

• Clouds are formed from condensation on dust and other particles above the ground.

• There are three major cloud forms—cumulus, stratus, and cirrus.

• There are four major forms of precipitation—rain, snow, sleet, and hail.

SECTION 2

Vocabulary

In your own words, write a definition of each of the following terms in the space provided.

1. air mass _____

_____

2. front _____

_____

Notes

Read the following section highlights. Then, in your own words, write the highlights in your ScienceLog.

• Air masses form over source regions. An air mass has similar temperature and moisture content throughout.

• Four major types of air masses influence weather in the United States—maritime polar, maritime tropical, continental polar, continental tropical.

• A front is a boundary between contrasting air masses.

• There are four types of fronts—cold fronts, warm fronts, occluded fronts, and stationary fronts.

• Specific types of weather are associated with each front.

SECTION 3

Vocabulary

In your own words, write a definition of each of the following terms in the space provided.

1. thunderstorm _____

_____

_____

2. lightning _____

_____

_____

3. thunder _____

_____

4. tornado _____

_____

_____

5. hurricane _____

_____

_____

Notes

Read the following section highlights. Then, in your own words, write the highlights in your ScienceLog.

• Severe weather is weather that can cause property damage and even death.

• Thunderstorms are small, intense storm systems that produce lightning, thunder, strong winds, and heavy rain.

• Lightning is a large electrical discharge that occurs between two oppositely charged surfaces.

• Thunder is the sound that results from the expansion of air along a lightning strike.

• A tornado is a rotating funnel cloud that touches the ground.

• Hurricanes are large, rotating, tropical weather systems that form over the tropical oceans.

SECTION 4
Vocabulary
In your own words, write a definition of each of the following terms in the space provided.

1. thermometer _____

_____

_____

2. barometer _____

_____

3. windsock _____

_____

4. wind vane _____

_____

5. anemometer _____

_____

6. isobars _____

_____

_____

Notes
Read the following section highlights. Then, in your own words, write the highlights in your ScienceLog.

• Weather balloons, radar, and weather satellites take weather measurements at high altitudes.

• Meteorologists present weather data gathered from stations as station models on weather maps.

CHAPTER

16 CHAPTER REVIEW WORKSHEET

Understanding Weather

USING VOCABULARY

For each pair of terms, explain the difference in their meanings.

1. relative humidity/dew point _____

_____

_____

_____

2. condensation/precipitation _____

_____

_____

3. air mass/front _____

_____

_____

_____

4. lightning/thunder _____

_____

_____

_____

5. tornado/hurricane _____

_____

_____

_____

6. barometer/anemometer _____

_____

_____

_____

UNDERSTANDING CONCEPTS

Multiple Choice

7. The process of liquid water changing to gas is called

   a. precipitation.

   b. condensation.

   c. evaporation.

   d. water vapor.

8. What is the relative humidity of air at its dew-point temperature?

   a. 0%

   b. 50%

   c. 75%

   d. 100%

9. Which of the following is NOT a type of condensation?

   a. fog

   b. cloud

   c. snow

   d. dew

10. High clouds made of ice crystals are called _____ clouds.

   a. stratus   **c.** nimbostratus

   b. cumulus   **d.** cirrus

11. Large thunderhead clouds that produce precipitation are called _____ clouds.

   a. nimbostratus   **c.** cumulus

   b. cumulonimbus   **d.** stratus

12. Strong updrafts within a thunderhead can produce

   a. snow.   **c.** sleet.

   b. rain.   **d.** hail.

13. A maritime tropical air mass contains

   a. warm, wet air.   **c.** warm, dry air.

   b. cold, moist air.   **d.** cold, dry air.

14. A front that forms when a warm air mass is trapped between cold air masses and forced high up into the atmosphere is called a(n)

   a. stationary front.   **c.** occluded front.

   b. warm front.   **d.** cold front.

15. A severe storm that forms as a rapidly rotating funnel cloud is called a

   a. hurricane.   **c.** typhoon.

   b. tornado.   **d.** thunderstorm.

16. The lines on a weather map connecting points of equal atmospheric pressure are called

   a. contour lines.   **c.** isobars.

   b. highs.   **d.** lows.

Understanding Weather, continued

Short Answer

17. Explain the relationship between condensation and the dew point.

_____

_____

_____

_____

_____

18. Describe the conditions along a stationary front.

_____

_____

_____

_____

_____

19. What are the characteristics of an air mass that forms over the Gulf of Mexico?

_____

_____

_____

_____

_____

20. Explain how a hurricane develops.

_____

_____

_____

_____

_____

_____

CONCEPT MAPPING

21. Use the following terms to create a concept map: *evaporation, relative humidity, water vapor, dew, psychrometer, clouds, fog.*

_____

Understanding Weather, continued

_____

CRITICAL THINKING AND PROBLEM SOLVING

Write one or two sentences to answer the following questions:

22. If both the air temperature and the amount of water vapor in the air change, is it possible for the relative humidity to stay the same? Explain.

_____

_____

_____

23. What can you assume about the amount of water vapor in the air if there is no difference between the wet- and dry-bulb readings of a psychrometer?

_____

_____

_____

24. List the major similarities and differences between hurricanes and tornadoes.

_____

_____

_____

MATH IN SCIENCE

You always see lightning before you hear thunder. That's because light travels at about 300,000,000 m/s, while sound travels only 330 m/s. One way you can determine how close you are to the thunderstorm is by counting how many seconds there are between the lightning and thunder. Usually, it takes thunder about 3 seconds to cover 1 km. Answer the following questions based on this estimate.

25. If you hear thunder 12 seconds after you see the flash of lightning, how far away is the thunderstorm?

_____

_____

26. If you hear thunder 36 seconds after you see the flash of lightning, how far away is the thunderstorm?

_____

_____

Understanding Weather, continued

INTERPRETING GRAPHICS

Use the weather map below to answer the questions that follow.

Warm front
Cold front
Stationary front

27. Where are thunderstorms most likely to occur? Explain your answer.

_____

_____

_____

28. What are the weather conditions like in Tulsa, Oklahoma? Explain your answer.

_____

_____

_____

NOW WHAT DO YOU THINK?

Take a minute to review your answers to the ScienceLog questions at the beginning of this chapter. Have your answers changed? If necessary, revise your answers based on what you have learned since you began this chapter.

CHAPTER

17 VOCABULARY & NOTES WORKSHEET

Climate

By studying the Vocabulary and Notes listed for each section below, you can gain a better understanding of this chapter.

SECTION 1

Vocabulary

In your own words, write a definition of each of the following terms in the space provided.

1. weather _____

_____

2. climate _____

_____

3. latitude _____

_____

4. prevailing winds _____

_____

5. elevation _____

_____

6. surface currents _____

_____

Notes

Read the following section highlights. Then, in your own words, write the highlights in your ScienceLog.

• Weather is the condition of the atmosphere at a particular time and place. Climate is the average weather conditions in a certain area over a long period of time.

• Climate is determined by temperature and precipitation.

• Climate is controlled by factors such as latitude, elevation, wind patterns, local geography, and ocean currents.

• The amount of solar energy an area receives is determined by the area's latitude.

• The seasons are a result of the tilt of the Earth's axis and its path around the sun.

• The amount of moisture carried by prevailing winds affects the amount of precipitation that falls.

• As elevation increases, temperature decreases.

• Mountains affect the distribution of precipitation. The dry side of the mountain is called the rain shadow.

Climate, continued

• As ocean currents move across the Earth, they redistribute warm and cool water. The temperature of the surface water affects the air temperature.

SECTION 2

Vocabulary

In your own words, write a definition of each of the following terms in the space provided.

1. biome _____

_____

_____

2. tropical zone _____

_____

_____

3. temperate zone _____

_____

_____

4. deciduous _____

_____

_____

_____

5. evergreens _____

_____

_____

6. polar zone _____

_____

_____

7. microclimate _____

_____

_____

Notes

Read the following section highlights. Then, in your own words, write the highlights in your ScienceLog.

- The Earth is divided into three climate zones according to latitude—the tropical zone, the temperate zone, and the polar zone.
- The tropical zone is the zone around the equator. The tropical rain forest, tropical desert, and tropical savanna are in this zone.
- The temperate zone is the zone between the tropical zone and the polar zone. The temperate forest, temperate grassland, chaparral, and temperate desert are in this zone.
- The polar zones are the northernmost and southernmost zones. The taiga and tundra are in this zone.

SECTION 3

Vocabulary

In your own words, write a definition of each of the following terms in the space provided.

1. ice age _____

_____

_____

2. global warming _____

_____

_____

3. greenhouse effect _____

_____

_____

_____

Notes

Read the following section highlights. Then, in your own words, write the highlights in your ScienceLog.

- Explanations for the occurrence of ice ages include changes in the Earth's orbit, volcanic eruptions, changes in the sun's energy output, and plate tectonics and continental drift.
- Some scientists believe that global warming is occurring as a result of an increase in carbon dioxide from human activity.
- If global warming continues, it could drastically change climates, causing either floods or drought.

CHAPTER

17 | CHAPTER REVIEW WORKSHEET

Climate

USING VOCABULARY

To complete the following sentences, choose the correct term from each pair of terms listed below, and write the term in the space provided.

1. _____ is the condition of the atmosphere in a certain area over a long period of time. (Weather or Climate)

2. _____ is the distance north and south from the equator measured in degrees. (Longitude or Latitude)

3. Savannas are grasslands located in the _____ zone between 23.5° north latitude and 23.5° south latitude. (temperate or tropical)

4. Trees that lose their leaves are found in a _____ forest. (deciduous or evergreen)

5. Frozen land in the polar zone is most often found in a _____. (taiga or tundra)

6. A rise in global temperatures due to an increase in carbon dioxide is called _____. (global warming or the greenhouse effect)

UNDERSTANDING CONCEPTS

Multiple Choice

7. The tilt of Earth as it orbits around the sun causes
   a. global warming.
   b. different seasons.
   c. a rain shadow.
   d. the greenhouse effect.

8. What factor affects the prevailing winds as they blow across a continent, producing different climates?
   a. latitude
   b. mountains
   c. forests
   d. glaciers

9. What factor determines the amount of solar energy an area receives?
   a. latitude
   b. wind patterns
   c. mountains
   d. ocean currents

10. What climate zone has the coldest average temperature?
    a. tropical
    b. polar
    c. temperate
    d. tundra

11. What biome is not located in the tropical zone?
    a. rain forest
    b. savanna
    c. chaparral
    d. desert

12. What biome contains the greatest number of plant and animal species?

    a. rain forest   **c.** grassland

    b. temperate forest   **d.** tundra

13. Which of the following is NOT a theory for the cause of ice ages?

    a. the Milankovitch theory

    b. volcanic eruptions

    c. plate tectonics

    d. the greenhouse effect

14. Which of the following is thought to contribute to global warming?

    a. wind patterns

    b. deforestation

    c. ocean surface currents

    d. microclimates

Short Answer

15. Why do higher latitudes receive less solar radiation than lower latitudes?

_____

_____

_____

_____

_____

16. How does wind influence precipitation patterns?

_____

_____

_____

_____

_____

_____

17. Give an example of a microclimate. What causes the unique temperature and precipitation characteristics of this area?

_____

_____

_____

_____

Climate, continued

_____

18. How have desert plants and animals adapted to this biome?

_____

_____

_____

_____

19. How are tundra and deserts similar?

_____

_____

CONCEPT MAPPING

20. Use the following terms to create a concept map: *climate, global warming, deforestation, greenhouse effect, flooding.*

CHAPTER 17

_____

Climate, continued

_____

CRITICAL THINKING AND PROBLEM SOLVING

Write one or two sentences to answer the following questions:

21. Explain how ocean surface currents are responsible for milder climates.

_____

_____

_____

_____

_____

22. In your own words, explain how a change in the Earth's orbit can affect the Earth's climates as proposed by Milutin Milankovitch.

_____

_____

_____

23. Explain why the climate differs drastically on each side of the Rocky Mountains.

_____

_____

_____

_____

_____

24. What are some steps you and your family can take to reduce the amount of carbon dioxide that is released into the atmosphere?

_____

_____

_____

_____

_____

Climate, continued

_____

MATH IN SCIENCE

25. If the air temperature near the shore of a lake measures 24°C, and if the temperature increases by 0.05°C every 10 m traveled away from the lake, what would the air temperature be 1 km from the lake?

_____

_____

_____

INTERPRETING GRAPHICS

Use the illustration on page 475 of your textbook to help answer the questions that follow. The illustration shows the Earth's orbit around the sun.

26. At what position, 1, 2, 3, or 4, is it spring in the Southern Hemisphere?

_____

27. At what position does the South Pole receive almost 24 hours of daylight?

_____

28. Explain what is happening in each climate zone in both the Northern Hemisphere and Southern Hemisphere at position 4.

_____

_____

_____

_____

_____

_____

_____

_____

_____

_____

NOW WHAT DO YOU THINK?

Take a minute to review your answers to the ScienceLog questions at the beginning of this chapter. Have your answers changed? If necessary, revise your answers based on what you have learned since you began this chapter.

Observing the Sky

By studying the Vocabulary and Notes listed for each section below, you can gain a better understanding of this chapter.

SECTION 1

Vocabulary

In your own words, write a definition for the following terms in the space provided.

1. astronomy _____

_____

2. calendar _____

_____

_____

3. year _____

_____

4. month _____

_____

5. day _____

_____

6. leap year _____

_____

Notes

Read the following section highlights. Then, in your own words, write the highlights in your ScienceLog.

- Calendars are based on movements of objects in the sky.
- Many ancient civilizations developed calendars.
- Our modern calendar developed from the Roman calendar.
- There is evidence all around the world for ancient astronomical observations.
- The Ptolemaic theory states that Earth is at the center of the universe, while Copernicus's theory states that the sun is at the center of the universe.
- Isaac Newton was the first scientist to explain why celestial objects move as they do.
- Galileo's use of the telescope brought the technology of astronomy to a new level.

SECTION 2

Vocabulary

In your own words, write a definition for the following terms in the space provided.

1. constellation _____

_____

2. altitude _____

_____

3. right ascension _____

_____

_____

_____

4. declination _____

_____

5. celestial equator _____

_____

6. ecliptic _____

_____

7. light-year _____

_____

Notes

Read the following section highlights. Then, in your own words, write the highlights in your ScienceLog.

• Astronomers divide the sky into 88 sections called constellations.

• Different constellations are visible from different locations, at different times of the year, and at different times of night.

• Star patterns appear as they do because of Earth's position in space. Most stars that appear close together are actually very far apart.

• The north celestial pole, the celestial equator, the zenith, and the horizon are imaginary markers used to locate objects in the sky.

• Right ascension and declination, which are similar to latitude and longitude, give coordinates of objects in the sky.

• Astronomers measure the distance to most objects in the universe in light-years.

• The size and distance of celestial objects detected in the universe can be difficult to determine. Scale must always be considered.

SECTION 3
Vocabulary

In your own words, write a definition for the following terms in the space provided.

1. telescope _____

_____

_____

2. refracting telescope _____

_____

3. reflecting telescope _____

_____

4. electromagnetic spectrum _____

_____

Notes

Read the following section highlights. Then, in your own words, write the highlights in your ScienceLog.

• Telescopes collect and focus electromagnetic radiation.

• Humans can see only visible light. To detect other wavelengths of radiation, astronomers use special telescopes or detectors.

• Types of telescopes include optical, radio, ultraviolet, infrared, X-ray, and gamma-ray.

• Some telescopes are launched into space to avoid the blurring effects of Earth's atmosphere or to collect radiation that can't penetrate Earth's atmosphere.

• Telescopes are often linked together to function as one giant telescope.

CHAPTER

18 CHAPTER REVIEW WORKSHEET

Observing the Sky

USING VOCABULARY

For each set of terms, explain the similarities and differences in their meanings.

1. reflecting telescope/refracting telescope _____

_____

_____

_____

_____

_____

_____

2. celestial equator/horizon _____

_____

_____

_____

_____

_____

_____

3. X rays/microwaves _____

_____

_____

_____

_____

_____

_____

_____

CHAPTER 18

Observing the Sky, continued

---

4. right ascension/declination _____

_____

_____

_____

_____

_____

_____

5. leap year/light-year _____

_____

_____

_____

UNDERSTANDING CONCEPTS

Multiple Choice

6. The length of a day is based on
   a. the Earth orbiting the sun.
   b. the rotation of the Earth on its axis.
   c. the moon orbiting the Earth.
   d. the rotation of the moon on its axis.

7. Which of the following civilizations directly affected the development of our modern calendar?
   a. The Chinese
   b. The Maya
   c. The Romans
   d. The Polynesians

8. According to _____, the Earth is at the center of the universe.
   a. the Ptolemaic theory
   b. Copernicus's theory
   c. Galileo's theory
   d. None of the above

9. The first scientist to successfully use a telescope to observe the night sky was
   a. Tycho.
   b. Galileo.
   c. Herschel.
   d. Kepler.

10. Astronomers divide the sky into
  a. galaxies.
  b. constellations.
  c. zeniths.
  d. phases.

11. The stars that you see in the sky depend on
  a. your latitude.
  b. the time of year.
  c. the time of night.
  d. All of the above

12. The altitude of an object in the sky is its angular distance
  a. above the horizon.
  b. from the north celestial pole.
  c. from the zenith.
  d. from the prime meridian.

13. Right ascension is a measure of how far east an object in the sky is from
  a. the observer.
  b. the vernal equinox.
  c. the moon.
  d. Venus.

14. Telescopes that work grounded on the Earth include all of the following except
  a. radio telescopes.
  b. refracting telescopes.
  c. X-ray telescopes.
  d. reflecting telescopes.

15. Which of the following is true about X-ray and radio radiation from objects in space?
  a. Both types of radiation can be observed with the same telescope.
  b. Separate telescopes are needed to observe each type of radiation, and both telescopes can be on Earth.
  c. Separate telescopes are needed to observe each type of radiation, and both telescopes must be in space.
  d. Separate telescopes are needed to observe each type of radiation, but only one of the telescopes must be in space.

Short Answer

Write one or two sentences to answer the following questions:

16. Explain how right ascension and declination are similar to latitude and longitude.

_____

_____

_____

_____

17. How does a reflecting telescope work?

_____

_____

_____

_____

CONCEPT MAPPING

18. Use the following terms to create a concept map: *celestial sphere, hours, celestial equator, declination, degrees, vernal equinox, right ascension.*

Observing the Sky, continued

CRITICAL THINKING AND PROBLEM SOLVING

19. Why was it easier for people in ancient cultures to see heavenly objects in the sky than it is for most people today?

_____

_____

_____

20. Many forms of radiation do not penetrate Earth's atmosphere. While this limits astronomer's activities, how does it benefit humans in general?

_____

_____

_____

MATH IN SCIENCE

21. How many kilometers away is an object whose distance is 8 light-years?

_____

_____

INTERPRETING GRAPHICS

Examine the sky map below, and answer the questions that follow. (Hint: The star Aldebran is located at about 4 hours, 30 minutes right ascension, 16 degrees declination.)

Celestial Coordinates

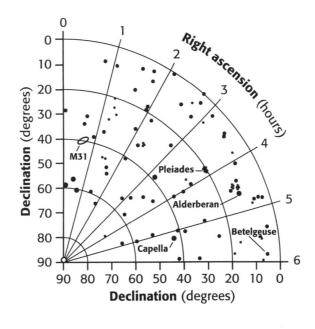

22. What object is located at 5 hr, 55 min right ascension and 7 degrees declination?

_____

_____

23. What are the celestial coordinates for the Andromeda galaxy (M31)? (Round off right ascension to the nearest half-hour.)

_____

_____

NOW WHAT DO YOU THINK?

Take a minute to review your answers to the ScienceLog questions at the beginning of the chapter. Have your answers changed? If necessary, revise your answers based on what you have learned since you began this chapter. Record your revisions in your ScienceLog.

19 VOCABULARY & NOTES WORKSHEET

Formation of the Solar System

By studying the Vocabulary and Notes for each section below, you can gain a better understanding of this chapter.

SECTION 1

Vocabulary

In your own words, write a definition for each of the following terms in the space provided.

1. solar system _____

_____

_____

2. nebula _____

_____

3. solar nebula _____

_____

4. planetesimal _____

_____

_____

5. rotation _____

_____

6. orbit _____

_____

7. revolution _____

_____

8. period of revolution _____

_____

_____

▲ CHAPTER 19

9. ellipse _____

_____

_____

_____

10. astronomical unit (AU) _____

_____

_____

_____

Notes

Read the following section highlights. Then, in your own words, write the highlights in your ScienceLog.

- The solar system formed out of a vast cloud of cold gas and dust called a nebula.
- Gravity and pressure were balanced, keeping the cloud unchanging until something upset the balance. Then the nebula began to collapse.
- Collapse of the solar nebula caused heating in the center. As material crowded closer together, planetesimals began to form.
- The central mass of the nebula became the sun. Planets formed from the surrounding disk of material.
- It took about 10 million years for the solar system to form, and it is now 4.6 billion years old.
- The orbit of one body around another has the shape of an ellipse.
- Planets move faster in their orbits when they are closer to the sun.
- The square of the period of revolution of the planet is equal to the cube of its semi-major axis.
- Gravity depends on the masses of the interacting objects and the square of the distance between them.

SECTION 2

Vocabulary

In your own words, write a definition for each of the following terms in the space provided.

1. corona _____

_____

_____

_____

Formation of the Solar System, continued

2. chromosphere _____

_____

_____

3. photosphere _____

_____

_____

4. convective zone _____

_____

_____

5. radiative zone _____

_____

_____

6. core _____

_____

7. nuclear fusion _____

_____

_____

_____

8. sunspot _____

_____

_____

_____

Notes

Read the following section highlights. Then, in your own words, write the highlights in your ScienceLog.

• The sun is a gaseous sphere made primarily of hydrogen and helium.

• The sun produces energy in its core by a process called nuclear fusion.

• Magnetic changes within the sun cause sunspots and solar flares.

SECTION 3

Vocabulary

In your own words, write a definition for each of the following terms in the space provided.

1. crust _____

_____

_____

_____

2. mantle _____

_____

_____

_____

3. core _____

_____

_____

Notes

Read the following section highlights. Then, in your own words, write the highlights in your ScienceLog.

• The Earth is divided into three main layers—crust, mantle, and core.

• Materials with different densities separated because of melting inside Earth. Heavy elements sank to the center because of Earth's gravity.

• Earth's original atmosphere formed from gases brought to Earth by meteorites and comets.

• Earth's second atmosphere arose from comet impacts and volcanic eruptions. The composition was largely water and carbon dioxide.

• The presence of life dramatically changed Earth's atmosphere, adding free oxygen.

• Earth's oceans formed shortly after the Earth did, when it had cooled off enough for rain to fall.

• Continents were formed when lighter materials gathered on the surface and rose above sea level.

CHAPTER

19 CHAPTER REVIEW WORKSHEET

Formation of the Solar System

USING VOCABULARY

For each pair of terms, explain the difference in their meanings.

1. rotation/revolution _____

_____

_____

_____

2. ellipse/circle _____

_____

_____

_____

_____

3. solar system/solar nebula _____

_____

_____

_____

_____

_____

4. planetesimal/planet _____

_____

_____

_____

5. temperature/pressure _____

_____

_____

_____

CHAPTER 19

Formation of the Solar System, continued

6. photosphere/corona _____

_____

_____

To complete the following sentences, choose the correct term from each pair of terms below, and write the term in the space provided.

7. It takes millions of years for light energy to travel through the sun's

_____ . (radiative zone or convective zone)

8. _____ of the Earth causes night and day.
(Rotation or Revolution)

9. Convection in Earth's mantle causes _____ .
(plate tectonics or nuclear fusion)

UNDERSTANDING CONCEPTS

Multiple Choice

10. Impacts in the early solar system

    a. brought new materials to the planets.   **c.** dug craters.

    b. released energy.   **d.** All of the above

11. Which type of planet will have a higher overall density?

    a. one that forms close to the sun

    b. one that forms far from the sun

12. Which process releases the most energy?

    a. nuclear fusion   **c.** shrinking due to gravity

    b. burning

13. Which of the following planets has the shortest period of revolution?

    a. Pluto   **c.** Mercury

    b. Earth   **d.** Jupiter

14. Which gas in Earth's atmosphere tells us that there is life on Earth?

    a. hydrogen   **c.** carbon dioxide

    b. oxygen   **d.** nitrogen

15. Which layer of the Earth has the lowest density?

    a. the core   **c.** the crust

    b. the mantle

16. What is the term for the speed of gas molecules?

    a. temperature   **c.** gravity

    b. pressure   **d.** force

17. Which of the following objects is least likely to have a spherical shape?

    a. a comet   **c.** the sun

    b. Venus   **d.** Jupiter

Formation of the Solar System, continued

Short Answer

18. Why did the solar nebula begin to collapse to form the sun and planets if the forces of pressure and gravity were balanced?

_____

_____

_____

19. How is the period of revolution related to the semimajor axis of an orbit? Draw an ellipse and label the semimajor axis.

_____

_____

20. How did our understanding of the sun's energy change over time?

_____

_____

_____

_____

_____

CHAPTER 19

CONCEPT MAPPING

21. Use the following terms to create a concept map: *solar nebula, solar system, planetesimals, sun, photosphere, core, nuclear fusion, planets, Earth.*

CRITICAL THINKING AND PROBLEM SOLVING

22. Explain why nuclear fusion works inside the sun but not inside Jupiter, which is also made mostly of hydrogen and helium.

_____

_____

_____

_____

_____

23. Why is it less expensive to launch an interplanetary spacecraft from the international space station in Earth's orbit than from Earth itself?

_____

_____

_____

_____

24. Soon after the formation of the universe, there was only hydrogen and helium. Heavier elements, such as carbon, oxygen, silicon, and all the matter that makes up the heavier minerals and rocks in the solar system, were made inside an earlier generation of stars. Do you think the first generation of stars had any planets like Earth, Venus, Mercury, and Mars? Explain.

_____

_____

_____

_____

MATH IN SCIENCE

25. Suppose astronomers discover a new planet orbiting our sun. The orbit has a semi-major axis of 2.52 AU. What is the planet's period of revolution?

_____

_____

_____

_____

CHAPTER 19

Formation of the Solar System, continued

26. If the planet in the previous question is twice as massive as the Earth but is the same size, how much would a person who weighs 100 lb on Earth weigh on this planet?

_____

_____

_____

INTERPRETING GRAPHICS

Look at the picture on page 533 of your textbook, and answer the questions that follow.

27. Do you think this is a rocky, inner planet or a gas giant?

_____

_____

_____

28. Did this planet form close to the sun or far from the sun? Explain.

_____

_____

_____

_____

_____

29. Does this planet have an atmosphere? Why or why not?

_____

_____

_____

NOW WHAT DO YOU THINK?

Take a minute to review your answers to the ScienceLog questions at the beginning of the chapter. Have your answers changed? If necessary, revise your answers based on what you have learned since you began this chapter. Record your revisions in your ScienceLog.

CHAPTER

20 **VOCABULARY & NOTES WORKSHEET**

A Family of Planets

By studying the Vocabulary and Notes listed for each section below, you can gain a better understanding of this chapter.

SECTION 1

Vocabulary

In your own words, write a definition for each of the following terms in the space provided.

1. astronomical unit (AU) _____

_____

_____

_____

2. terrestrial planets _____

_____

3. prograde rotation _____

_____

_____

_____

4. retrograde rotation _____

_____

_____

_____

5. gas giants _____

_____

Notes

Read the following section highlights. Then, in your own words, write the highlights in your ScienceLog.

• The solar system has nine planets.

• Distances within the solar system can be expressed in astronomical units (AU) or in light-minutes.

CHAPTER 20

_____ **A Family of Planets, continued** _____

- The inner four planets, called the terrestrial planets, are small and rocky.
- The outer planets, with the exception of Pluto, are gas giants.
- By learning about the properties of the planets, we get a better understanding of global processes on Earth.

SECTION 2

Vocabulary

In your own words, write a definition for each of the following terms in the space provided.

1. satellite _____

_____

_____

_____

2. phases _____

_____

_____

_____

3. eclipse _____

_____

_____

_____

Notes

Read the following section highlights. Then, in your own words, write the highlights in your ScienceLog.

- Earth's moon probably formed from a giant impact on Earth.
- The moon's phases are caused by the moon's orbit around the Earth. At different times of the month, we view different amounts of sunlight on the moon because of the moon's position relative to the sun and the Earth.
- Lunar eclipses occur when the Earth's shadow falls on the moon.
- Solar eclipses occur when the moon is between the sun and the Earth, causing the moon's shadow to fall on the Earth.
- The plane of the moon's orbit around the Earth is tilted by 5° relative to the plane of the Earth's orbit around the sun.

SECTION 3

Vocabulary

In your own words, write a definition for each of the following terms in the space provided.

1. comet _____

_____

_____

_____

_____

_____

_____

_____

2. asteroid _____

_____

_____

_____

_____

_____

_____

_____

3. asteroid belt _____

_____

_____

_____

_____

_____

_____

CHAPTER 20

4. meteoroid _____

_____

_____

_____

5. meteorite _____

_____

_____

_____

6. meteor _____

_____

_____

_____

_____

Notes

Read the following section highlights. Then, in your own words, write the highlights in your ScienceLog.

• Comets are small bodies of rock, ice, and cosmic dust left over from the formation of the solar system.

• When a comet is heated by the sun, the ices convert to gases that leave the nucleus and form an ion tail. Dust also comes off a comet to form a second kind of tail called a dust tail.

• All orbits are ellipses—circles that have been stretched out.

• Asteroids are small, rocky bodies that orbit the sun between the orbits of Mars and Jupiter.

• Meteoroids are small, rocky bodies that probably come from asteroids.

• Meteor showers occur when Earth passes through the dusty debris along a comet's orbit.

• Impacts that cause natural disasters occur once every few thousand years, but impacts large enough to cause global extinctions occur once every 30 million to 50 million years.

CHAPTER

20 **CHAPTER REVIEW WORKSHEET**

A Family of Planets

USING VOCABULARY

For each pair of terms, explain the difference in their meanings.

1. terrestrial planet/gas giant _____

_____

_____

_____

2. asteroid/comet _____

_____

_____

_____

3. meteor/meteorite _____

_____

_____

_____

_____

4. satellite/moon _____

_____

_____

_____

_____

5. Kuiper belt/Oort cloud _____

_____

_____

_____

_____

CHAPTER 20

To complete the following sentences, choose the correct term from each pair of terms listed below, and write the term in the space provided.

6. The average distance between the sun and the Earth is

1 _____ . (light-minute or AU)

7. A small rock in space is called a _____ .
(meteorite, meteor, or meteoroid)

8. The time it takes for the Earth to _____ around the sun is one year. (rotate or revolve)

9. Most lunar craters are the result of _____ .
(volcanoes or impacts)

UNDERSTANDING CONCEPTS

Multiple Choice

10. When do annular eclipses occur?
  a. every solar eclipse
  b. when the moon is closest to the Earth
  c. only during full moon
  d. when the moon is farthest from the Earth

11. Of the following, which is the largest body?
  a. the moon
  b. Pluto
  c. Mercury
  d. Ganymede

12. Which is NOT true about impacts?
  a. They are very destructive.
  b. They can bring water to dry worlds.
  c. They only occurred as the solar system formed.
  d. They can help us do remote geology.

13. Which of these planets does not have any moons?
  a. Mercury
  b. Mars
  c. Uranus
  d. None of the above

14. What is the most current theory for the formation of Earth's moon?
  a. The moon formed from a collision between another body and the Earth.
  b. The moon was captured by the Earth.
  c. The moon formed at the same time as the Earth.
  d. The moon formed by spinning off from the Earth early in its history.

15. Liquid water cannot exist on the surface of Mars because
  a. the temperature is too hot.
  b. liquid water once existed there.
  c. the gravity of Mars is too weak.
  d. the atmospheric pressure is too low.

16. Which of the following planets is NOT a terrestrial planet?

    a. Mercury

    b. Mars

    c. Earth

    d. Pluto

17. All of the gas giants have ring systems.

    a. true

    b. false

18. A comet's ion tail consists of

    a. dust.

    b. electrically charged particles of gas.

    c. light rays.

    d. comet nuclei.

Short Answer

19. Do solar eclipses occur at the full moon or at the new moon? Explain why.

20. How do we know there are small meteoroids and dust in space?

21. Which planets have retrograde rotation?

CONCEPT MAPPING

22. Use the following terms to create a concept map: *solar system, terrestrial planets, gas giants, moons, comets, asteroids, meteoroids.*

CRITICAL THINKING AND PROBLEM SOLVING

23. Even though we haven't yet retrieved any rock samples from Mercury's surface for radiometric dating, we know that the surface of Mercury is much older than that of Earth. How do we know this?

_____

_____

_____

_____

_____

A Family of Planets, continued

24. Where in the solar system might we search for life, and why?

_____

_____

_____

_____

25. Is the far side of the moon always dark? Explain your answer.

_____

_____

_____

_____

_____

26. If we could somehow bring Europa as close to the sun as the Earth is, 1 AU, what do you think would happen?

_____

_____

_____

_____

_____

MATH IN SCIENCE

27. Suppose you have an object that weighs 200 N (45 lbs.) on Earth. How much would that same object weigh on each of the other terrestrial planets?

_____

_____

_____

_____

CHAPTER 20

A Family of Planets, continued

INTERPRETING GRAPHICS

The graph below shows density versus mass for Earth, Uranus, and Neptune. Mass is given in Earth masses—the mass of Earth equals one. The relative volumes for the planets are shown by the size of each circle.

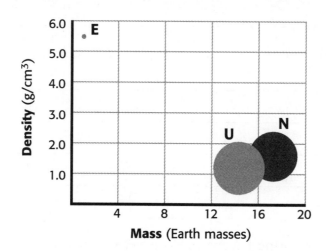

Density vs. Mass for Earth, Uranus, and Neptune

28. Which planet is denser, Uranus or Neptune? How can you tell?

_____

_____

_____

_____

29. You can see that although Earth has the smallest mass, it has the highest density. How can Earth be the densest of the three when Uranus and Neptune have so much more mass?

_____

_____

_____

_____

NOW WHAT DO YOU THINK?

Take a minute to review your answers to the ScienceLog questions at the beginning of the chapter. Have your answers changed? If necessary, revise your answers based on what you have learned since you began this chapter. Record your revisions in your ScienceLog.

CHAPTER

21 VOCABULARY & NOTES WORKSHEET

The Universe Beyond

By studying the Vocabulary and Notes listed for each section below, you can gain a better understanding of this chapter.

SECTION 1

Vocabulary

In your own words, write a definition for each of the following terms in the space provided.

1. spectrum _____

_____

_____

2. apparent magnitude _____

_____

_____

3. absolute magnitude _____

_____

_____

4. light-year _____

_____

5. parallax _____

_____

Notes

Read the following section highlights. Then, in your own words, write the highlights in your ScienceLog.

- The color of a star depends on its temperature. Hot stars are blue. Cool stars are red.
- The spectra of stars indicate their composition. Spectra are also used to classify stars.
- The magnitude of a star is a measure of its brightness.
- Apparent magnitude is how bright a star appears from Earth.
- Absolute magnitude is how bright a star actually is. Lower absolute magnitude numbers indicate brighter stars.
- Distance to nearby stars can be measured by their movement relative to stars farther away.

SECTION 2

Vocabulary

In your own words, write a definition for each of the following terms in the space provided.

1. H-R diagram _____

_____

_____

_____

2. main sequence _____

_____

_____

3. white dwarf _____

_____

_____

4. red giant _____

_____

5. supernova _____

_____

6. neutron star _____

_____

_____

_____

7. pulsar _____

_____

8. black hole _____

_____

_____

_____

The Universe Beyond, continued

Notes
- New stars form from the material of old stars that have gone through their life cycles.
- The H-R diagram relates the temperature and brightness of a star. It also illustrates the life cycle of stars.
- Most stars are main-sequence stars. Red giants and white dwarfs are later stages in a star's life cycle.
- Massive stars become supernovas. Their cores turn into neutron stars or black holes.

SECTION 3

Vocabulary

In your own words, write a definition for each of the following terms in the space provided.

1. galaxy _____

_____

2. spiral galaxy _____

_____

3. elliptical galaxy _____

_____

4. irregular galaxy _____

_____

5. nebula _____

_____

6. open cluster _____

_____

7. globular cluster _____

_____

_____

8. quasar _____

_____

_____

_____

Notes

Read the following section highlights. Then, in your own words, write the highlights in your ScienceLog.

- Edwin Hubble classified galaxies according to their shape. Major types include spiral, elliptical, and irregular galaxies.

- A nebula is a cloud of gas and dust. New stars are born in some nebulas.

- Open clusters are groups of stars located along the spiral disk of a galaxy. Globular star clusters are found in the halos of spiral galaxies and in elliptical galaxies.

- Because light travels at a certain speed, observing distant galaxies is like looking back in time. Scientists look at distant galaxies to learn what early galaxies look like.

SECTION 4

Vocabulary

In your own words, write a definition for each of the following terms in the space provided.

1. cosmology _____

_____

_____

_____

2. big bang theory _____

_____

_____

_____

3. cosmic background radiation _____

_____

_____

_____

Notes

- The big bang theory states that the universe began with an explosion about 10 billion to 15 billion years ago.

- Cosmic background radiation fills the universe with radiation that is left over from the big bang. It is supporting evidence for the big bang theory.

- Observations show that the universe is expanding outward. There is no measurable center and no apparent edge.

- All matter in the universe is a part of larger systems, from planets to superclusters of galaxies.

CHAPTER
21 | **CHAPTER REVIEW WORKSHEET**

The Universe Beyond

USING VOCABULARY

For each pair of terms, explain the difference in their meanings.

1. absolute magnitude/apparent magnitude _____

_____

_____

_____

_____

_____

2. spectrum/parallax _____

_____

_____

_____

_____

_____

_____

3. main-sequence star/red giant _____

_____

_____

_____

_____

_____

_____

4. white dwarf/black hole _____

_____

_____

_____

_____

_____

5. elliptical galaxy/spiral galaxy _____

_____

_____

_____

_____

_____

6. big bang/cosmic background radiation _____

_____

_____

_____

_____

_____

_____

UNDERSTANDING CONCEPTS

Multiple Choice

7. The majority of stars in our galaxy are
   a. blue.
   b. white dwarfs.
   c. main-sequence stars.
   d. red giants.

8. Which would be seen as the brightest star in the following group?
   a. Alcyone—apparent magnitude of 3
   b. Alpheratz—apparent magnitude of 2
   c. Deneb—apparent magnitude of 1
   d. Rigel—apparent magnitude of 0

9. A cluster of stars forms in a nebula. There are red stars, blue stars, yellow stars, and white stars. Which stars are most like the sun?
   a. red
   b. yellow
   c. blue
   d. white

10. Individual stars are moving in space. How long will it take to see a noticeable difference without using a telescope?

a. 24 hours
b. 1 year
c. 100 years
d. 100,000 years

11. You visited an observatory and looked through the telescope. You saw a ball of stars through the telescope. What type of object did you see?

a. a spiral galaxy
b. an open cluster
c. a globular cluster
d. a barred spiral galaxy

12. In which part of a spiral galaxy do you expect to find nebulas?

a. the central region
b. the nuclear bulge
c. the halo
d. all parts of the galaxy

13. Which statement about the big bang theory is accurate?

a. The universe will never end.
b. New matter is being continuously created in the universe.
c. The universe is filled with radiation coming from all directions in space.
d. We can locate the center of the universe.

Short Answer

14. Describe how the apparent magnitude of a star varies with its distance from Earth.

_____

_____

_____

15. Name six types of astronomical objects in the universe. Arrange them by size.

_____

_____

_____

_____

16. Which contains more stars on average, a globular cluster or an open cluster?

_____

_____

_____

The Universe Beyond, continued

17. What does the big bang theory have to say about how the universe will end?

_____

_____

_____

_____

_____

_____

CONCEPT MAPPING

18. Use the following terms to create a concept map: *black hole, neutron star, main-sequence star, red giant, nebula, white dwarf.*

CRITICAL THINKING AND PROBLEM SOLVING

Write one or two sentences to answer the following questions:

19. If a certain star displayed a large parallax, what could you say about its distance from Earth?

_____

_____

20. Two M-type stars have the same apparent magnitude. Their spectra show that one is a red giant and the other is a red-dwarf star. Which one is farther from Earth? Explain your answer.

_____

_____

_____

21. Look back at the H-R diagram in Section 2. Why do astronomers use absolute magnitudes to plot the stars? Why don't they use apparent magnitudes?

_____

_____

_____

_____

22. While looking at a galaxy through a nearby university's telescope, you notice that there are no blue stars present. What kind of galaxy is it most likely to be?

_____

_____

_____

_____

MATH IN SCIENCE

23. An astronomer observes two stars of about the same temperature and size. Alpha Centauri B is about 4 light-years away, and sigma^2 Eridani A is about 16 light-years away. How much brighter does Alpha Centauri B appear?

_____

_____

The Universe Beyond, continued

INTERPRETING GRAPHICS

The following graph illustrates the Hubble law relating the distances of galaxies and their speed away from us.

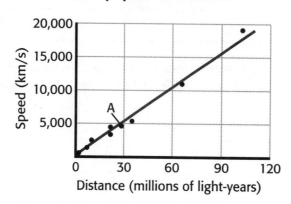

Galaxy Speed vs. Distance

24. Look at the galaxy marked A in the graph. What is its speed and distance?

_____

_____

25. If a new galaxy with a speed of 15,000 km/s were found, at what distance would you expect it to be?

_____

_____

NOW WHAT DO YOU THINK?

Take a minute to review your answers to the ScienceLog questions at the beginning of the chapter. Have your answers changed? If necessary, revise your answers based on what you have learned since you began this chapter. Record your revisions in your ScienceLog.

CHAPTER

22 VOCABULARY & NOTES WORKSHEET

Exploring Space

By studying the Vocabulary and Notes listed for each section below, you can gain a better understanding of this chapter.

SECTION 1
Vocabulary
In your own words, write a definition for the following terms in the space provided.

1. rocket _____

_____

2. NASA _____

_____

_____

3. thrust _____

4. orbital velocity _____

_____

5. escape velocity _____

_____

_____

Notes
Read the following section highlights. Then, in your own words, write the highlights in your ScienceLog.
- Two pioneers of rocketry were Konstantin Tsiolkovsky and Robert Goddard.
- Rockets work according to Newton's third law of motion—for every action there is an equal and opposite reaction.
- NASA was formed in 1958, combining rocket research from several programs. It was originally formed to compete with the Soviet Union's rocket program.

SECTION 2
Vocabulary
In your own words, write a definition for the following terms in the space provided.

1. artificial satellite _____

_____

2. low Earth orbit _____

_____

3. geosynchronous orbit _____

_____

_____

_____

_____

Notes

Read the following section highlights. Then, in your own words, write the highlights in your ScienceLog.

• The Soviet Union launched the first Earth-orbiting satellite in 1957. The first United States satellite went up in 1958.

• Low Earth orbits (LEOs) are located a few hundred kilometers above the Earth's surface. Satellites in geosynchronous orbits (GEOs) have an orbit period of 24 hours and remain over one spot.

• Satellite programs are used for weather observations, communications, mapping the Earth, and tracking ocean currents, crop growth, and urban development.

• One great legacy of the satellite program has been an increase in our awareness of the Earth's fragile environment.

SECTION 3

Vocabulary

In your own words, write a definition for the following terms in the space provided.

1. space probe _____

_____

Notes

Read the following section highlights. Then, in your own words, write the highlights in your ScienceLog.

• Planetary exploration with space probes began with missions to the moon. The next targets of exploration were the inner planets: Venus, Mercury, and Mars.

• The United States has been the only country to explore the outer solar system, beginning with the *Pioneer* and *Voyager* missions.

• Space-probe science has given us information about how planets form and develop, helping us to better understand our own planet Earth.

SECTION 4
Vocabulary
In your own words, write a definition for the following terms in the space provided.

1. space shuttle _____

_____

2. space station _____

_____

_____

Notes
Read the following section highlights. Then, in your own words, write the highlights in your ScienceLog.

- The great race to get a manned flight program underway and to reach the moon was politically motivated.
- The United States beat the Soviets to a manned moon landing with the Apollo moon flights in 1969.
- During the 1970s, the United States focused on developing the space shuttle. The Soviets focused on developing orbiting space stations.
- The United States, Russia, and 14 other international partners are currently developing the *International Space Station*.
- Because of scientific, economic, and even recreational reasons, humans may eventually live and work on other planets and moons.

CHAPTER 22

Exploring Space

USING VOCABULARY

For each pair of terms, explain the difference in their meaning:

1. geosynchronous orbit/low Earth orbit _____

_____

_____

_____

_____

_____

2. space probe/space shuttle _____

_____

_____

_____

_____

_____

_____

3. artificial satellite/moon _____

_____

_____

_____

To complete the following sentences, choose the correct term from each pair of terms listed below:

4. The force that accelerates a rocket is called _____ . (escape velocity or thrust)

5. Rockets need to have _____ in order to burn their fuel. (oxygen or nitrogen)

UNDERSTANDING CONCEPTS

Multiple Choice

6. The father of modern rocketry is considered to be

   a. K. Tsiolkovsky.   **c.** W. von Braun.

   b. R. Goddard.   **d.** D. Eisenhower.

7. Rockets work according to Newton's

   a. first law of motion.

   b. second law of motion.

   c. third law of motion.

   d. law of universal gravitation.

8. The first artificial satellite to orbit the Earth was

   a. *Pioneer 4.*   **c.** *Voyager 2.*

   b. *Explorer 1.*   **d.** *Sputnik 1.*

9. Satellites are able to transfer TV signals across and between continents because they

   a. are located in GEOs.

   b. relay signals past the horizon.

   c. travel quickly around Earth.

   d. can be used day and night.

10. GEOs are better orbits for communications because satellites in GEO

   a. remain in position over one spot.

   b. are farther away from Earth's surface.

   c. do not revolve around the Earth.

   d. are only a few hundred kilometers high.

11. Which space probe discovered evidence of water at the moon's south pole?

   a. *Luna 9*

   b. *Viking 1*

   c. *Clementine*

   d. *Magellan*

12. When did humans first set foot on the moon?

   a. 1949   **c.** 1969

   b. 1959   **d.** 1979

13. Which one of these planets has not yet been visited by space probes?

   a. Mercury

   b. Neptune

   c. Mars

   d. Pluto

14. Of the following, which space probe is about to leave our solar system?

   a. *Galileo*   **c.** *Mariner 10*

   b. *Magellan*   **d.** *Pioneer 10*

CHAPTER 22

15. Based on space-probe data, where is the most likely place in our solar system to find liquid water?

    a. the moon   **c.** Europa

    b. Mars   **d.** Titan

Short Answer

Write one or two sentences to answer the following questions:

16. Describe how Newton's third law of motion relates to the movement of rockets.

_____

_____

_____

_____

_____

_____

_____

_____

17. What is one disadvantage that objects in LEO have?

_____

_____

_____

18. Why did the United States develop the space shuttle?

_____

_____

_____

19. During which period were spy satellites first used?

_____

_____

CONCEPT MAPPING

20. Use the following terms to create a concept map: *orbital velocity, escape velocity, thrust, low Earth orbit, artificial satellites, space probes, geosynchronous orbit, rockets.*

CRITICAL THINKING AND PROBLEM SOLVING

21. What is the difference between speed and velocity?

_____

_____

_____

22. Why must rockets that travel in outer space carry oxygen with them?

_____

_____

_____

23. How will data from the space probes help us to understand the Earth's environment?

_____

_____

_____

_____

MATH IN SCIENCE

24. Why was it necessary for several nations to work together to create the *ISS*?

_____

_____

_____

25. In order to escape the Earth's gravity, a rocket must travel at least 11 km/s. This is pretty fast! If you could travel to the moon at this speed, how many hours would it take you to get there? (The moon is about 384,000 km away from the Earth.) Round your answer to the nearest whole number.

_____

_____

_____

Exploring Space, continued

INTERPRETING GRAPHICS

The map on page 621 of your text book was made using satellite data. It indicates the different amounts of chlorophyll in the ocean. Chlorophyll, in turn, identifies the presence of marine plankton. The blues and purples show the smallest amount of chlorophyll, and the reds and oranges show the most. Examine the map, and answer the questions that follow.

26. At which location, A or B, are more plankton concentrated?

_____

27. What do you conclude about the conditions in which plankton prefer to live?

_____

_____

_____

_____

NOW WHAT DO YOU THINK?

Take a minute to review your answers to the ScienceLog questions at the beginning of the chapter. Have your answers changed? If necessary, revise your answers based on what you have learned since you began this chapter. Record your revisions in your ScienceLog.